THE SUN

THE SUN

by Karl Kiepenheuer

ANN ARBOR

THE UNIVERSITY OF MICHIGAN PRESS

PREFACE

Our sun is a star, and the only star whose shape and surface can be observed. All other stars remain mere glimmers of light in even the largest telescope, and the nature of that light can only be deduced by rather indirect ways. Thus, solar research plays a special part within the framework of astrophysics. The sun is our bridge to the stars.

In this book I have endeavored to emphasize and illustrate the peculiarities of this star, the sun. I am very grateful to my publishers for having agreed to include so many photographs.

Many facets of the rapid developments in solar research have had to be omitted, since I have striven for clarity rather than completeness. The very sun which shines on us so radiantly out of a blue sky can also be a battlefield of opposing, abstract theories. I have tried to keep out of this battle, though occasionally I have tacitly taken sides.

The complex interrelations between the sun and the earth have only been touched upon. They deserve a book on their own.

K.O.K.

CONTENTS

THE SUN

1. Introduction

> It is true, I never assisted the sun
> materially in his rising, but, doubt
> not, it was of the last importance only
> to be present at it.
> —Henry David Thoreau.

The astronomer's sun differs greatly from the layman's, for where the latter sees a brilliant disk spreading
light, warmth, and well-being, the astronomer sees a
star of class G, or a hydrogen sphere with a surface
temperature of approximately 10,800°F. This sphere
does not rotate as a solid body, and its surface is studded
with spots, faculae, and prominences. In this book I
shall try to explain this astronomical sun to you.

Solar physics is a branch of astrophysics, though it
uses many special methods. The sun is, after all, the
only star which, because of its relatively short distance
from the earth, has a visible surface and shape. All other
stars are mere points of light in even the largest telescope. Thus, where the solar astronomer can rely on his
telescope, the astrophysicist can only examine the quality
of light emitted by the stars. Hence his conclusions are
often more theoretical and indirect. This fact makes the
sun an object of paramount importance, for our observations of the solar atmosphere provide important data
about the behavior of the stellar universe at large.

The solar atmosphere is known almost as intimately as our own. Unfortunately, conditions on the sun are such that we cannot simply apply our own meteorological findings to it. Because of the sun's high temperature, its different chemical composition, and the impossibility of simulating solar conditions in the laboratory, the solar physicist has to rely on theoretical physics and must avoid judging from terrestrial conditions.

Matters are much more difficult still when it comes to the sun's interior. Here we must rely on atomic theory, and our picture is always a reflection of our current knowledge of that theory and, like it, must constantly be modified. Solar physics and physics are therefore intimately related, and the serious reader would do well, if need be, to consult a popular textbook on physics.

In this book, you will get to know a star. The phenomena are so complex that the total picture of the sun may easily be lost sight of. I shall therefore begin with a bird's-eye view of solar astronomy to which the reader is advised to refer if ever he loses the thread of the argument.

Solar physics in 2000 words

The sun is one among a host of stars, that is, it is a gaseous body with a diameter of 864,000 miles and a mass of 2.10^{33} grams. Its distance from the earth is 93,000,000 miles, and light takes eight minutes to travel this distance. Under favorable conditions, the best solar telescopes reveal surface details down to a diameter of about 300 miles. Seen from the earth, the sun takes roughly four weeks to rotate on its axis. Strangely enough, it does not rotate like a solid body, for while the equator takes roughly 27 days to rotate, the polar regions take about 30 days. For thousands of millions of years, the sun's surface (which is at a temperature of about 10,800°F.) has been emitting 4.10^{23} kilowatts of energy per second in the form of light (electromagnetic waves). The source of this energy lies deep within the sun, where the temperature is about 15,000,000°. Roughly 90 per cent of the energy comes from the region 0–0.23 r (r = radius of sun), where the density is 100 grams per cubic centimeter. This region represents 40 per cent of the total mass of the sun (Fig. 1). The energy is derived from the transmutation of hydrogen into helium, one gram of hydrogen supplying roughly 200,000 kilowatt hours.

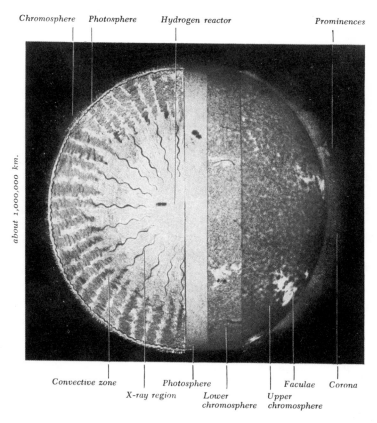

Chromosphere   *Photosphere*   *Hydrogen reactor*   *Prominences*

about 1,000,000 km.

Convective zone   *Photosphere*   *Faculae*   *Corona*

X-ray region   *Lower chromosphere*   *Upper chromosphere*

FIG. 1. Model of the sun. Right: The different layers composed from photographs. Left: Section through the sun.

This energy is broadcast outward in the form of X and γ rays in such a way that an equal quantity of energy flows through every concentric shell drawn about the center of the sun. If we draw a shell at a distance 0.7 r from the center, conditions have become such (temperature: 234,000°F.; density: 0.07 grams per cubic centimeter) that radiation alone can no longer maintain this flow of energy. Like water boiling in a kettle, the solar matter begins to seethe and carries its own heat to the surface. The area between 0.7 and 1.0 r is therefore known as the convective zone. Within this zone the density drops until it reaches 10^{-8} grams per cubic centimeter at the surface, and the temperature falls to about 9000°F.

At the surface the boiling mass assumes the shape of granules (irregular convection cells), each with a diameter of about 600 miles, and with an internal flow at the rate of about one mile a second. This upper layer is called the *photosphere*. For us it is the source of all sunlight.

Some 6000 miles above the photosphere, the density has rapidly decreased from 10^{-8} grams per cm^3 to 10^{-11} grams per cm^3, and to 10^{-16} grams per cm^3 some 12,000 miles higher up (the atmospheric density at the surface of the earth is $\approx 10^{-3}$ grams per cm^3). The light reaching us from these higher, rarefied strata is consequently so weak that it can only be observed with instruments which eliminate the glare of the photosphere.

Immediately above the photosphere lies the *chromosphere* or "color sphere." It has a depth of up to 6000 miles and, more turbulent than the photosphere, it is a constantly seething mass of gases. We may call the upper chromosphere the spray of the photosphere which—in a way not yet fully understood—is thrown up by the rising photospheric granules with velocities greater than six miles a second.

Unlike the terrestrial atmosphere, therefore, the chromosphere is not in static equilibrium. The temperature of this seething mass of froth and gaseous fountains is somewhat greater than the temperature of the photosphere.

At the outer edge of the chromosphere the density suddenly drops to 1/1000 the mean chromospheric density. Here, we find the *corona*, a gigantic layer of rarefied gases which stretches for millions of miles into space. The corona is directly visible only during total eclipses, when the moon hides the sun from view (Fig. 33). Its temperature is roughly 1,800,000°F.—much hotter than the chromosphere. In other words the kettle is hotter than the stove.

Even so, it would be wrong to imagine that the chromosphere heats the corona as a stove heats a kettle. What happens is that some kinetic energy escapes from the chromosphere into the corona by way of so-called shock-waves (supersonic pressure waves), and it is this kinetic energy which raises the temperature of the rarefied gases. In fact the temperature in the corona is so high that the coronal hydrogen nuclei (protons) completely lose their planetary electrons. Heavy nuclei such as carbon, nitrogen, and oxygen may lose up to 15 of their electrons.

The corona (which accounts for only 10^{-15} of the sun's total mass) is probably partly made up of interplanetary matter (dust and meteors). The constant gravitational pull of matter into the corona is probably balanced by constant solar evaporation into space.

The restless sun

The energy represented by the changes we shall now discuss is insignificant when compared with the radiation sent out by the sun. Changes in the appearance of the sun follow a rhythm of roughly 11 or 22 years, though the so-called solar cycle is not strictly periodic. The more striking changes occur mainly in certain limited latitudes of the solar surface which, in the course of one solar cycle, undergo a characteristic drift. The many individual phenomena are best understood if they are thought to originate from a common center of activity, for example from a solar storm which—like a storm on earth—brings winds, rain, thunder, and lightning in its wake.

Such solar storms or centers of activity—more than ten may occur at the same time—can be observed simultaneously in the photosphere, the chromosphere, and the corona. Unlike terrestrial storms, they affect even deeper, hidden layers, where their true source must be sought. The fact that centers of activity undergo a systematic latitude drift points to the existence of large-scale currents in the interior of the sun. These currents are closely related to the sun's uneven rotation. In fact, we have every reason to believe that the turbulence caused by the uneven rotation is the real motor of all solar activity.

The primary disturbance rises from the solar interior in the form of a restricted magnetic field (or more precisely as a volume of gas with a magnetic field). The upper photosphere, and the chromosphere beyond, then display the first storm signals: bright faculae, that is, superheated incandescent clouds of gas. Meanwhile, dark spots have formed among the granules of the photosphere. These spots represent regions some hundreds of miles in diameter, in which the temperature is about 2700°F. lower than in the surrounding neighborhood.

The spots increase quickly both in number and in magnitude to form a group of sunspots (see Fig. 38). Spots are associated with strong magnetic fields and represent centers of intensive atmospheric activity. With the growth of spots there is a corresponding growth in the magnitude and brightness of faculae. Flares appear for minutes or hours according to their area (see Fig. 52). Flares emit visible light, ultraviolet rays, and X rays.

Furthermore, flares are frequently accompanied by the ejection of invisible clouds of gas which reach the earth approximately one day later (their velocity is about 600 miles a second) to disturb the terrestrial magnetic field. At the same time as the flares, elongated clouds are formed in the vicinity of every group of spots. These clouds can only be observed with special instruments (they are almost transparent in white sunlight) through which they look like smoke against the solar disk. They are then known as filaments. When seen on the limb—the edge of the sun—these long clouds, which stand out brightly against the dark background of the sky, are called prominences. While sunspots generally fade away after a few weeks, and faculae lose their brilliance after about two months, filaments keep growing for many months, finally to form into structures up to 600,000 miles in length. These structures are among the most stable of all the many solar surface phenomena.

Occasionally, and sometimes associated with chromospheric flares, the filaments break up and are shot out into space. Strangely enough, they reform after a few days to resume their old shape. Their reorganization is probably due to magnetic phenomena, the charged particles in the solar atmosphere following the sun's magnetic field as a compass needle follows a magnet.

Solar storms reach up into the corona. Its temperature and luminosity increase strongly in the vicinity of the centers of activity, to whose number and position the total form is closely related. If these are few and far between, the corona is flattened and has marked equatorial wings. When the activity is strongest, however, the corona has a spherical form with rays in all directions.

As a rough measure of solar activity, sunspots have been counted daily for the last 300 years (Wolf's relative sunspot number).

Before discussing modern solar research, we must quickly see what historical developments have led to the contemporary picture, the better to appreciate which men and what ideas have most affected it.

Short history of solar research

450 B.C.   Heraclides was the first to suggest that some of the planets revolve about the sun. He still held that the sun itself revolves about the earth.

190– 125 B.C.   Hipparchus rejected the idea that planets are freely suspended in space and introduced the notion of crystal spheres. The inventor of trigonometry, he introduced celestial co-ordinates, made a list of 1080 fixed stars, and explained that the motion of moon and sun result from epicyclic movements. He was the first to fix a position on the earth by astronomical measurement of latitude and longitude, and was the father of scientific astronomy.

140 A.D.   Ptolemy upheld Hipparchus' findings and published his famous handbook of astronomy, the *Almagest*, containing tables which give the position of the planets. (The book reached Europe in the eighth century, and a Greek version was first printed five years after Copernicus published his work.) Ptolemy realized that the notion of epicyclic movements cannot fully account for the motion of the planets.

1475– 1543   Nicolaus Copernicus placed the sun in the center of the universe, the earth being one of the five known planets. The first draft of his *De revolutionibus orbium coelestius* was completed in 1530 and published in 1542. Copernicus explained his system as follows: "The first and highest of all spheres is that of the fixed star, containing as it does itself in addition to all the others, hence forming the immobile *centrum mundi* to which the motion and position of all other heavenly bodies must be referred. Next comes Saturn, the first of the planets, which completes its course in thirty years, then Jupiter which takes twelve years to run its full course, then Mars which runs its course in two years. The fourth place is occupied by the annual orbit of the earth which contains the earth and the orbit of the moon which is its epicycle. In the fifth place, Venus circles the sun in nine months. The sixth place is occupied by Mercury, which completes its course in eighty days. In the midst of all stands the sun, for in this beautiful temple, who would have set that bright jewel into another or better place than that from which it can illuminate the whole at once?" Copernicus still thought that all the planets revolve in concentric circles about the sun.

1546–1601   The Danish astronomer Tycho Brahe, rejecting the Copernican model, attempted to effect a reconciliation between the view of the church and Ptolemy's cosmology. While the planets revolve about the sun, the sun itself revolves about the earth. The sphere of fixed stars, the sun, and the moon revolve about the earth, the center of the universe. Brahe improved observational methods by using large sextants and collected a tremendous number of valuable data on the motion of the planets.

1608   Invention of the telescope by Lippersheim in Holland.

1609   Johannes Kepler (1571–1630) used Tycho Brahe's observations of Mars to formulate his laws of planetary motion.

1610   Galileo in Padua and Johannes Fabricius in Wittenberg independently discovered sunspots and their motion across the sun.

1611   Christoph Scheiner in Ingolstadt also discovered sunspots, but was taken to task by his superior for "seeing things that cannot be found in Aristotle." He was afraid to make further observations during the next 6 months.

1616   Despite Galileo's objections, Copernicus' work was placed on the Index in Rome.

1632   Pope Urban VIII prosecuted the 70-year-old Galileo.

1640   Descartes suggested that space is filled with a transparent medium which drags the whole planetary system with it.

1666   Newton discovered the law of universal gravitation and applied it to the motion of the planets.

1675   Ole Rømer calculated the velocity of light from observations of the moons of Jupiter.

1746	Claude Simeon was the first to drive an equatorially mounted telescope by clockwork.
1802	Wollaston discovered dark lines in the solar spectrum.
1814	Fraunhofer, using an improved spectrograph, discovered the first 547 Fraunhofer lines in the solar spectrum.
1820	Invention of photography.
1849	Wolf introduced his "sunspot number."
1851	The first photograph of the corona during a total eclipse.
1852	Wolf and Gautier discovered the intimate relation between the sunspot cycle and geomagnetic storms.
1858	Carrington showed that the distribution of spots in latitude shifts with the sunspot cycle.
1859–61	Kirchhoff and Bunsen explained the origin of the dark Fraunhofer lines in the solar spectrum.
1868	Lockyer and Janssen used special apparatus to observe prominences near the limb. (Formerly, prominences could only be observed during eclipses of the sun.)
1888	Langley used a bolometer to record the solar spectrum from the ultraviolet to the extreme infrared.
1889	G. E. Hale, then 21 years old, invented the spectrohelioscope and in 1891 obtained the first reliable spectroheliogram of the sun.
1897	Rowland completed his atlas of the solar spectrum.
1900	Planck discovered the law of "black radiation."
1901	Deslandres and Oliver Lodge failed to receive Hertzian waves from the sun.
1905	Einstein discovered light quanta.
1908	Hale discovered magnetic fields in the sunspots. The solar origin of terrestrial magnetic storms was explained.
1913	Niels Bohr interpreted the spectrum of the hydrogen atom.
1929	Russell used spectroscopic observations to discover the chemical composition of the sun.
1930	Lyot used his coronagraph to observe the corona without an eclipse.
1937	Jansky received radio waves from the Milky Way.
1940	Edlén interpreted the emission lines of the corona.

1942   The radio emission of the sun was detected by radar.

1946   Demonstration of the solar component of cosmic radiation.

1950   Solar radiation in the extreme ultraviolet and in the X-ray range was measured by rockets outside the terrestrial atmosphere.

II. The Solar System

Position in the universe

Through the world's largest (200-inch) reflecting telescope on Mount Palomar in California we can look at space up to 200,000,000,000 light years away. This space is almost uniformly populated with about 260,000,000 galaxies, all of rather similar form and all receding from us swiftly. The fastest of these galaxies (whose velocities we can only just make out from their spectrum) fly into space at a rate of about 26,000 miles per second, that is, one-seventh the velocity of light. These galaxies are about 200,000,000 light years away from us. At the furthest distance reached by the Mount Palomar telescope, the gigantic galaxies, each of which is made up of at least 10,000,000,000 stars, shrink into mere points of light that can just be distinguished from their neighbors. Their light is greatly dimmed by the weak glow of our own atmosphere.

At the center of this *observable* sphere lies our own galaxy, one among 260,000,000. Like many other galaxies, it is a spiral nebula. This was proved quite recently from the study of cosmic radio waves. (Cosmic radio waves give a more reliable indication of interstellar matter than does the light from the stars, since radio waves within our galaxy, unlike ordinary light, are not greatly weakened by the clouds of interstellar dust.)

Seen laterally, our galaxy looks like a disk, with a diameter of about 100,000 light years and a maximum depth of about 10,000 light years (Fig. 2). The sun, one among 10,000,000,000 stars in our galaxy, lies close to the equatorial plane, about 30,000 light years from the center (Fig. 3). Our entire galaxy is in rotation, the sun moving with a velocity of 175 miles a second in the direction of Cygnus. The sun completes one revolution about the center of the galaxy in about 250,000,000 years. As a consequence of the galactic rotation, the sun moves, with respect to its brighter neighbors, at a rate of about 11 miles per second toward Hercules.

The mean distance between the stars is roughly one light year (10^{18} cm), while the diameter of a single star is only about 10^{11} cm. The stellar diameter is therefore minute compared with the distance between two stars. Our galaxy is practically empty.

All the same, the investigation of light from distant stars has shown that interstellar space is filled with very small quantities of matter. In our own galaxy the density of interstellar matter is of the order of one atom per cubic centimeter. Interstellar matter exists in the form of clouds of gas or dust which whirl about with a velocity of a few miles per second. Toward the galactic center, the clouds of dust begin to thicken, thus hiding the center from view. In the vicinity of the sun and near the orbits of the planets the density is approximately 1000 atoms per cubic centimeter. This is still a very insignificant number if we consider that air at sea

FIG. 2. Spiral nebulae resembling our own galaxy. Top: Spiral nebula in Ursus Major. Bottom: Profile of spiral nebula in Coma Berenices. (Photographs: Mt. Wilson Observatory.)

level contains roughly 10^{19} atoms per cubic centimeter. The space between the stars is, therefore, very transparent.

The planets

Our sun has nine planets, most of which are much larger than the earth. The distance between the sun and Pluto, the furthest planet, is very small compared with

	MERCURY	VENUS	EARTH	MARS	JUPITER	SATURN	URANUS	NEPTUNE	PLUTO
Mean distance from sun (earth's distance = 1)	0.39	0.72	1.00	1.52	5.2	9.5	19.2	30.2	39.5
Period of revolution (in years)	0.241	0.615	1.00	1.88	11.9	29.5	84.0	164.8	
Inclination of orbit to ecliptic	7°0'	3°24'	0°0'	1°51'	1°18'	2°19'	0°46'	1°47'	17°1'
Eccentricity of orbit	0.206	0.007	0.017	0.093	0.048	0.056	0.047	0.009	0.249
Diameter in miles	3000	7600	7900	4200	88,700	75,100	30,900	33,000	3,600
Mass in terms of the earth's mass	0.037	0.83	1.00	0.11	318.4	95.2	14.6	16.9	0.03
Surface gravity (earth = 1)	0.26	0.90	1.00	0.38	2.64	1.13	0.96	1.00	0.5

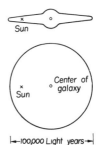

FIG. 3. The position of our sun in the galaxy.

the distance between the sun and the nearest star, the orbital diameter of Pluto being 1/200,000 of the mean distance between stars in the Milky Way. A distant observer would therefore be unable to see the planets through the intense glare of the sun. The table on page 24 lists the orbits and properties of the nine planets.

The table and also Figs. 4 and 5 give some idea of the magnitudes involved. The total mass of all the planets is $445 \times$ the mass of the earth and about 1 per cent the mass of the sun. The mean distance between the sun and the earth (called 1.0 in the table) is 93,000,000 miles. The inclination of the planetary orbits to the ecliptic is very small, all planets moving nearly in a plane.

The motions of the planets with respect to the fixed stars has been the subject of astronomical and astrological speculation for thousands of years. Johannes Kepler (1609) was the first to formulate the laws of planetary motion in a simple and clear manner. Using the great wealth of observational data compiled by Tycho Brahe, Kepler derived his laws empirically. He followed Copernicus in rejecting the assumption that the earth was the immobile center of the universe and proposed that the heavenly bodies, because of their divine greatness, were bound to describe the most perfect geometric figures, that is, circles. In the year 1609,

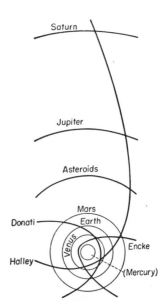

FIG. 4. The orbits of planets, asteroids, and some comets.

FIG. 5. Against the background of the sun with spots, prominences, and filaments are shown Saturn with its ring and satellites (center), Jupiter with its 12 satellites (left), Mercury, Venus, Earth, and Mars (top left), and Uranus, Neptune, and Pluto with their satellites (right).

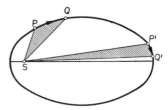

FIG. 6. Kepler's second law.

publishing his "true laws of planetary motion," he said: "At last I have brought to light, and shown with certainty beyond all my hopes and expectations, that the whole nature of harmonies in all its scope and in every detail is reflected in the celestial motions, not, it is true, in the way I formerly thought it to be but in an entirely different, absolutely perfect manner."

Kepler's three famous laws are:

1. The planets travel in elliptical orbits, the sun being at one focus.

2. A line drawn from the planet to the sun sweeps equal areas in equal times. (This is clearly seen from Fig. 6. Near the sun, the planet will have to travel more quickly to sweep the same area.)

3. The ratio $\dfrac{(\text{Period of revolution})^2}{(\text{Mean distance from sun})^3}$ is the same for all the planets. (Were the planets to revolve in circles, the square of the planet's periodic time would be proportional to the cube of the radius.)

The third law was discovered by Kepler in 1618: "It was on the 8th March of this year 1618, if the exact time be of interest, that the law came to my mind. But luck was not with me, for when I checked it with calculations, I rejected it as false. Finally, it came back to me on the 15th May, and vanquishing the darkness of my spirit, it caused such wonderful agreement to appear between my labors during the past seventeen years on Brahe's observations and my present reflections that I first thought I had dreamed it and had simply presupposed the desired result in the final proof."

While Kepler's first law fixes the *form* of the planetary orbits, the second governs the velocities of the planets on these orbits. The third law enables us to calculate the distances of the planets from the sun, once the distance of one planet (the earth) and the period of revolution of the other planet is known. The second law, in particular, establishes a close connection between the sun and the motion of the planets. In fact this had been at the back of Kepler's mind during the long years of painstaking search leading to discovery of his laws. Thus he wrote: "I am replacing celestial theology by celestial philosophy or celestial physics" and "Formerly I was firmly convinced that the cause of the planetary motion was a spiritual principle. . . . When, however, I noticed that the cause of motion waned with distance from the sun, I had to conclude that it was a force of a material nature."

Almost a hundred years later (in 1683) Isaac Newton (1643–1727) had the brilliant idea—perhaps the greatest of all cosmological ideas—that the same force that caused an apple to fall from a tree acted on all bodies in space. From this he concluded that the moon's circular orbit about the earth was due to the force of gravity, which, reaching the moon from the earth through empty space, attracted it just as it attracted objects on the surface of the earth. Then Newton formulated his law of universal gravitation: "Every portion of matter in the universe attracts every other portion with a force which is proportional directly to the product of their masses, and inversely to the square of their distance apart." Newton soon showed that Kepler's laws, and particularly his first and third laws, were the direct consequence of the law of universal gravitation. With Newton's simple law, celestial mechanics had at last been given a firm foundation. Strangely enough, Newton, though he had arrived at it as early as 1666, did not publish his law until 1687. Strange also that his thoughts were first turned to gravitation by the plague, which forced him to leave Cambridge and to interrupt his intensive work on optics and on second fluxions (repeated differentiation) which was then taking up his entire attention.

So far, we have discussed the geometric properties of the planets. Now, the planets, just like the earth, are physical entities with striking surface phenomena. These are, however, very difficult to observe through the telescope, particularly since observations are impeded by uneven heating effects in the terrestrial atmosphere. As a result, the tiny planetary disks look blurred and distorted. For the same reason it is impossible, for instance, to recognize details smaller than 300 miles on the solar surface, or smaller than 300 feet on our (much closer) moon.

A great deal of reliable information on the physical and chemical properties of planetary surfaces and atmospheres can be deduced from the nature of reflected sunlight. The following is a brief survey of the astronomical and physical properties of the planets.

Mercury: This planet nearest to the sun is not much larger than our moon. Mercury cannot be seen with the naked eye during the hours of bright sunlight, and this fact, together with thermal interference by the terrestrial atmosphere, makes observations extremely difficult. Because of its small mass, Mercury must have a very thin atmospheric shell. Mercury's surface temperature is probably about 392°F., and its orbit does not strictly obey Kepler's law. The deviations were interpreted by Einstein's relativity theory, and were in fact used as experimental evidence for that theory.

Venus: Next to moon and sun, Venus is the brightest object in our sky, and can even cast shadows on earth. We see it as the morning and evening star. Venus is nearer the sun than the earth and has a surface temperature of about 145°F. Its surface is hidden from view by dense whitish-yellow cloud formations which reflect about 70 per cent of the sunlight—hence the brightness. The atmosphere contains a great deal of carbon dioxide but probably no free oxygen. The planet's period of rotation on its own axis is uncertain.

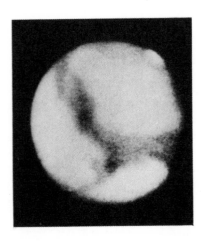

FIG. 7. Mars.

Earth: The earth resembles Venus both in size and in distance from the sun. To an outside observer from another planet, the earth (which reflects 43 per cent of the incident sunlight) would look as bright as Mars. His telescope would occasionally be able to pick out land and ocean masses, large cloud formations and seasonal color changes. No doubt, the earth would display the most changeable surface of all the planets. Traces of human activity could be detected very occasionally and under particularly favorable conditions, but no detail smaller than 40 miles across could be distinguished.

Mars: Mars has a ruddy appearance. It is further from the sun than the earth and takes about two years to revolve. Hence its distance from us, and thus its brightness and apparent diameter, keep changing. Every seventeen years Mars approaches very close to the earth (this happened last in 1956) when it looks like a disk with a diameter of 8 inches seen at a distance of a mile (Fig. 7). Mars is half as big as the earth, and its day is almost as long as one of ours. Its atmosphere is much more highly rarefied than that of the earth, the atmospheric temperature ranging from − 40 to + 77°F. The atmosphere contains little or no water-vapor, and small white clouds are an exceptional phenomenon. Extensive yellow dust storms may temporarily change the color of the entire planet. In the equatorial desert regions, the surface of Mars seems to resemble that of our moon. The white polar caps (only one of which is visible at a time) reflect infrared light and are believed to consist of ice at a very low temperature. It is not yet known definitely whether the green regions on Mars are the result of primitive cold-resisting plants (lichens) or of crystals that change color with the seasons. Two moons revolve about Mars, but these can only be seen through powerful telescopes.

Jupiter: This planet can be observed through a simple telescope. It is yellowish and never fainter than Sirius. Jupiter's distance from the sun is five times that of the earth. Jupiter has a period of twelve years. Its diameter is 88,700 miles—almost one-tenth the diameter of the sun. Its period of rotation is only 9 hours 50 minutes, and Jupiter is therefore considerably flattened at the poles (Fig. 8). Corresponding to its large mass, it has a very dense and extensive atmosphere containing large quantities of methane (marsh gas), ammonia, and hydrogen. The planet's surface is hidden behind dense, constantly

FIG. 8. Jupiter.

FIG. 10. Morehouse's Comet III photographed in 1908.

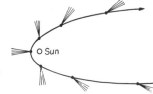

FIG. 11. Orientation of comets' tails.

Comets

The comets are another group of members of the solar system (Fig. 10). Recently they have once again attracted the attention of astrophysicists. In the Middle Ages they caused panic with consequent neglect of the fields and great famines. While they have lost their terror for the modern astronomer, they confront him with exceedingly difficult problems.

Comets are not often very impressive objects. They usually look like round clouds with a somewhat brighter center. In contradistinction to planets, comets revolve about the sun in ellipses with high eccentricities. Their periods range between a few years and a few thousand years, and the total number of comets in the solar system is thought to be greater than a thousand. As a comet approaches the sun, its nucleus, consisting of an immense number of small particles, is heated by the sun's rays and begins to exude gases (mainly hydrocarbons). The moment these gases leave the nucleus, they are acted upon by a strong force that drives them away from the sun—hence, the notorious tail which generally points away from the sun (Fig. 11). Until quite recently, it was thought that the tail was the result of solar radiation pressure on the exuded gases. This explanation was shown to rest on fallacious assumptions about the radiation pressure of ultraviolet sunlight. It is now believed that the tails are deflected by "cosmic wind" (a stream of protons and electrons) which blows radially from the sun into interstellar space with a velocity of a few hundred miles per second. Its density, however, is extremely small—about 1000 protons and electrons per cubic centimeter. These particles are continuously evaporated from the very hot solar corona (see p. 71). The tails of comets are therefore useful guides to the study of solar radiation in general, and comets have become the outposts of astrophysical studies not only of solar ultraviolet radiation but also of corpuscular emission.

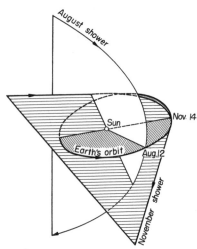

FIG. 12. The paths of meteor showers.

Meteors

Meteors are the smallest and most numerous members of the solar family. If, in their flight through space, they happen to penetrate our atmosphere, their great speed (about 18 miles per second) gives rise to frictional heat, so that they generally evaporate. When this happens they become shooting stars. Even tiny stones weighing only a few milligrams can produce visible light phenomena. Debris from the larger meteors, the so-called meteorites often manage to strike the surface of the earth. The origin of meteors has never been explained satisfactorily. Some observations point to their origin in interstellar space, while others point to the fact that meteors have always been part of the solar system. At certain times during the year the number of shooting stars increases steadily, so much so that hundreds of shooting stars can be observed during one hour. This happens because meteoric showers move round the sun in orbits with various eccentricities and at different inclinations to the ecliptic, thus approaching the earth at regular intervals. Figure 12 shows the orbits of the best known meteoric showers. Meteors have recently been observed—even by day—with radar equipment for detecting the direction and strength of the radio waves reflected by their ionized tails.

Dust and gas

Our description of the solar system would be incomplete without an account of the rarefied matter in the space between the planets. Recent investigations have shown that interplanetary matter is made up of gas and dust. While the gas occupies a large flattened sphere with the sun at its center, the dust apparently forms a

FIG. 13. The zodiacal light (drawing by Trouvelot).

flat ring about the sun in the plane of the planetary orbits. The space immediately near the sun is free of dust since here the heat of the sun evaporates all solid particles. Shortly after nightfall or just before the dawn, an observer in the shadow of the earth may sometimes witness the striking spectacle of zodiacal light. Zodiacal light is the result of the reflection of sunlight by interplanetary dust and electrons. It looks like a pyramid of light towering up over the horizon and may be as bright as the Milky Way. Figure 13 is a drawing of the zodiacal light made by E. L. Trouvelot 80 years ago.

III. *The Surface of the Sun*

Observation and magnitudes

Seen through a smoked glass, the sun looks like a tennis ball at a distance of fifteen yards. Therefore, it is almost impossible to pick out surface details with the naked eye. Nevertheless, larger groups of sunspots can occasionally be observed without a telescope, provided that thick mists or clouds veil the glare of the sun.

Through the telescope the sun looks like a brilliant off-white disk with a slightly darkened limb (Fig. 14). The darkening of the limb or edge gives the sun its spherical appearance. The entire disk displays fine structural details, with dark sunspots in the equatorial region and bright faculae near the limb.

The sun should not be observed directly through the telescope without proper protection. It is best to project its image on a fixed paper screen (Fig. 15). This method obviates the use of a black filter and avoids the consequent loss of intensity. If the telescope is focused to produce an image of 150 mm diameter, then 1 mm of the image represents 10,000 km on the surface of the sun. With this set-up, many solar details can be distinguished. The focal length of the telescope ought not to be less than 60 cm and the objective should have an aperture of at least 60 mm. Also, the objective should be a compound lens compensated for chromatic aberration.

But even the best telescope cannot project a perfect solar image, since the terrestrial atmosphere causes a marked flickering or scintillation. As the light from the sun strikes air particles of different temperatures the rays are scattered in all directions, with consequent loss of definition in the picture. There is no known remedy against these disturbing effects of the terrestrial atmosphere. Some observatories happen to have a "good" atmosphere, while others have not. Astronomers have a fair idea of the meteorological conditions needed for reliable observations.

Granulation

The visible surface of the sun is not uniformly bright (Fig. 14). If we look at it through telescopes with a

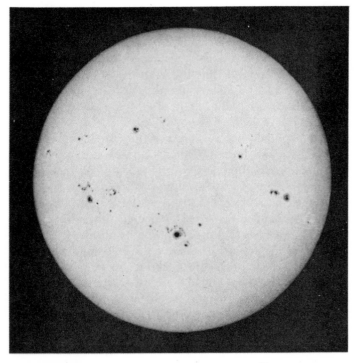

FIG. 14. The sun as it appears through the telescope.

FIG. 15. Solar telescope.

large magnification and under very good observational conditions, i.e., through "good" air, it appears to be cobbled with stones. Figure 16 is an excellent photograph of these "cobbles," the so-called granules. The photograph was taken as long ago as 1885 by Janssen in Paris. To make it perfectly clear that he had not retouched the negative, he added the following legend: "*Obtenue sans aucune intervention de la main humaine.*" Individual cobblestones have diameters of 375 to 950 miles and look like regular polygons. These gigantic "cells" have a mean life of a few minutes and keep dissolving and reforming. Clearly, the processes involved must be of a very violent nature, regions the size of Germany being built up and destroyed within a matter of minutes.

We can make a small-scale qualitative model of these processes. If we apply heat to a thin layer of oil the oil at the very bottom will rise to the top by convection. At the top, it gives up its heat to the air and sinks to the bottom again. This heat exchange gives rise to the formation of fairly regular hexagonal convection cells, in each of which the fluid rises in the center and flows down

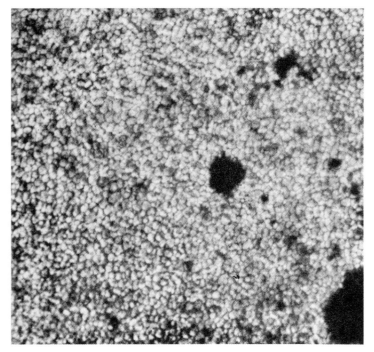

FIG. 16. Granulation photographed by Janssen in 1885.

along the edges. In Figure 17 this process has been made visible by the addition of fine aluminum powder. Similar convection currents can also be produced with cigarette smoke. A vessel is filled with smoke to the height of an electric wire (Fig. 18) and the current is switched on. The heat then produces the convection cells shown in the figure.

Such processes occur also in our own atmosphere, particularly in the case of alto-cumulus and cirro-cumulus clouds. While the external processes in the oil experiment, cumulus clouds, and solar granules are roughly similar, the forces giving rise to them are quite different. In our cigarette-smoke experiment, the con-vection currents were caused by the heating effect of

the electric wire. The explanation is far more complicated in the case of clouds. While dry air (the cigarette
smoke) cools quickly as it expands and rises, air taking
up water vapor cools far more slowly because it absorbs
heat from the condensing vapor. It will therefore have
a density below that of the surrounding air and keep
rising higher. The driving force here is the heat of
liquefaction.

Similar physical processes take place on the sun, although the currents and velocities involved are much
greater. In lower strata of the sun, hydrogen, the main
constituent of the solar atmosphere, is completely ionized
by the high temperature. Electrons from the atomic
nuclei—the protons—fly about freely. When they rise
to the solar surface, where the temperature is much
lower, they are recaptured by the protons there. During
this process heat is liberated, just as it is during the
condensation of water in air. As a result of this heat,
the granules have a smaller density than the surrounding solar atmosphere and keep rising higher. The rising photospheric granules are thus hotter, and hence
brighter, than their environment. This contrast produces
the granular appearance of the solar surface. Only 1 per

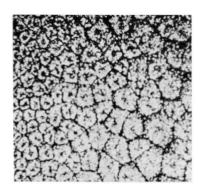

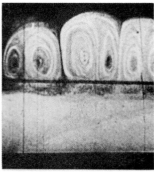

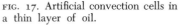

FIG. 17. Artificial convection cells in a thin layer of oil.

FIG. 18. Convection cells in cross section.

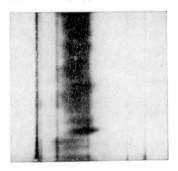

FIG. 19. Granular structure in hydrogen lines.

cent of the total energy radiated by the sun is needed for maintaining the granular convection-currents which turn the photosphere into a constantly changing field of contiguous whirlwinds. The wind velocities here are well over a thousand miles per hour, while in our own atmosphere, even during the worst hurricanes, they rarely exceed 200 miles an hour.

Since the Fraunhofer or line-spectrum of the sun (see page 53) originates from the same layer of the sun in which the granules are situated, attempts have recently been made to assess the current velocity of the granules from the Doppler effect (shift in the position of the lines as a result of the motion of the source of emission with respect to the observer). Figure 19 shows a spectrogram of the sun taken with a high-resolution vacuum spectrograph under particularly good atmospheric conditions. Every indentation of the lines corresponds to an individual granule. By means of spectroscopy, the velocity of the granules was found to be approximately 0.3 miles a second.

Theoretical considerations and model experiments have enabled astronomers to give a satisfactory interpretation of solar convection phenomena. Unfortunately, many other solar events which can be observed far better than granulation still await a strict physical interpretation.

IV. *Sunlight*

All light is emitted by atoms

Light is our only means of communication with the rest of the universe, so much so that astronomy and astrophysics might be called the decoding of light-messages from space.

All light, no matter whether from space, from an electric bulb, or from a glowworm, is emitted by atoms or by the even smaller electrons. For the effects of this light to be felt, or measured, it must impinge on, and be absorbed by, other atoms. This absorption of light can occur in exposure meters or photographic plates and can be felt by its effects on the retina of our eye. The path of stellar light for us is always the path between a cosmic and a terrestrial atom, and the astrophysicist has to deduce the physical state of the light-emitting atoms from their effect on terrestrial atoms. Basically, he relies on two properties of light: its intensity and its color. The first is a quantity, the second a quality.

The intensity of solar radiation

If we expose a black tin cup, filled with water, to the light of the sun, tin and water will become warm. The rise in temperature in unit time is a fair measure of the intensity of the radiation. Most instruments for measuring the strength of solar radiation are based on this simple idea. They are called pyrheliometers.

Long-term measurements in which care was taken to account for the weakening of the radiation by the terrestrial atmosphere (which, on a clear day, can be as high as 20 per cent) have shown that the sun throws roughly one kilowatt of radiant energy on every square meter of the earth. Put differently, the sun's heating effect on the earth is about .29 calories per square inch per minute. To warm up a small garden (¼ acre) in this way we should need roughly 1½ million calories, i.e., about 6 million watts.

The technical exploitation of solar radiation

In the final analysis, all terrestrial energy comes from the sun. Even the coal and oil with which we heat our homes and the gas with which we drive our cars are photochemical products of solar radiation. By its action on carbon, oxygen, and nitrogen, this radiation gave rise to chlorophyll and thus to plants which, in turn, became the carbon deposits from which we derive most of our fuels.

But solar radiation can also be exploited directly in the following ways:

1. The sun's rays are kept focused on a small vessel containing water, by means of a concave mirror. The resulting steam is used for driving a steam engine. The mechanical or electric energy produced has a maximum efficiency factor of 10 per cent. This set-up has little practical value.

2. The steam is used directly without being converted into mechanical or electric energy. It can be used for cooking or for canning. In the sunny parts of southern Russia, many canning plants are powered in this way. Many of the mirrors used have diameters of more than 10 meters and produce roughly 125 pounds of steam under a pressure of 7 atmospheres per hour. Another

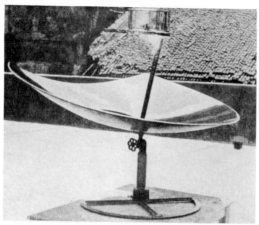

FIG. 20. Indian solar cooker.

arrangement makes it possible to distill up to 275 gallons of water per day and, by driving a cooling unit, to produce about 30 tons of ice per day. The Russians have also constructed solar kitchens for private use, in which a concave mirror with a diameter of 1 to 2 meters brings roughly a gallon of water an hour to the boil. These mirrors must be adjusted manually every half hour or so, to follow the direction of the sun. The average heating effect of such a solar kitchen is equivalent to that of a 600-watt electric element. Similar solar cookers are said to have been widely distributed by the Indian government (Fig. 20).

Solar energy is commonly used for heating houses. Ordinary window glass has the remarkable property of letting in approximately 90 per cent of the solar radiation and of retaining the heat radiated by the walls. Thus, glass windows are excellent traps of the sun's rays. This explains why sunny rooms are often so much warmer than the air outside.

3. Solar energy can be converted directly (without the agency of steam) into electric energy by means of

photoelectric cells or thermocouples. Unfortunately, the cost of this direct conversion is altogether out of proportion to the results so far obtained (efficiency rarely more than 10 per cent). It is reasonable to assume, however, that advances in semiconductor techniques will soon lead to considerable improvements.

Our carbon and uranium deposits are so vast that mankind has not yet felt forced to tackle the exploitation of solar energy seriously. In case of need technologists should have no difficulty in converting solar energy into electric currents.

Already, we have the so-called "solar-furnaces," in which highly concentrated solar radiation is used for investigating materials at temperatures which, produced in any other way, would cause contamination of the materials. Such furnaces are in use particularly in the southwestern states of America and in France.

The solar constant

Since the intensity of solar radiation was long thought to be stable, it was somewhat prematurely called "the solar constant." Later, it was found to fluctuate slightly, though rarely by more than 1 per cent. Some observers believe that the solar constant varies with the distribution of sunspots. However, this belief cannot stand up to critical investigation. In the last chapter, we shall return to these small fluctuations and their influence on the earth.

How hot is the sun?

Everyone knows that the hotter a metal (e.g., the radiant of an electric stove) the more energy it radiates. The relation between the temperature of a glowing body and the strength of the radiation it emits is given by the Stefan-Boltzmann law, which states that the emitted radiation varies with the fourth power of the absolute temperature ($W = KT^4$). Thus, if we double the temperature of our stove, it will emit 16 times its former radiation. We can use this law to deduce the temperature of the sun from the strength of the radiation which reaches us, always remembering that our instruments receive no more than a tiny fraction of it. This fraction can be calculated once the distance of the sun from the earth is known. Since the sun emits its energy equally in all directions (if this were not the case the energy would have to be lost or concentrated in space), we can imagine the energy as spreading through an infinite number of concentric circles drawn about the sun. If R is the radius of the earth's orbit about the sun, that is, the distance from the sun to the earth, the surface of this circle is $4\pi R^2$, while the surface of the sun itself is $4\pi r^2$, where r is the radius of the sun. Thus the radiation spreads out from a sphere of surface $4\pi r^2$ to one of surface $4\pi R^2$. Now since R is approximately 200 r, the radiation we receive is $1/200$ ^{2} or $1/40,000$ the radiation on the surface of the sun. To evaluate the true radiation, we must therefore multiply the observed radiation—the solar constant—by 40,000. From these calculations it appears that the sun must have a surface temperature of almost 11,000°F. To appreciate the magnitude of this figure, we need only recall that the temperature of red-hot iron is 1100°F. and that the white-hot filament of an electric bulb has a temperature of at most 3600°F. All known substances would quickly evaporate at so great a temperature, even carbon which is normally heat-resisting. It is for this reason that the sun is gaseous, despite the fact that its average density is 1.4 grams per cubic centimeter and despite the fact that matter on the sun has almost one and one-half times the weight of water.

Let us now go a step further, and investigate the temperature of individual regions on the sun's surface. A telescope is made to concentrate the rays from the sun on a screen in which a hole has been drilled. A

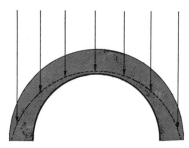

FIG. 21. Depths at which one can look into the solar atmosphere.

measuring instrument is placed behind the hole, and by moving the telescope, the radiant intensity of given areas on the sun can now be evaluated. It is found that the brightness of the disk decreases noticeably toward the limb. Figure 21 helps to explain this. It shows how deep into the sun the telescope can penetrate. If we point it on the center of the sun, we look at the solar atmosphere vertically and can therefore observe the greatest depth. Toward the limb, we look into the solar atmosphere at an ever-increasing slant, and must therefore cross ever-thicker layers of light-absorbing gases to penetrate to a given depth. Hence the apparent drop in temperature.

The radiant layer emitting white sunlight is called the photosphere. Telescopic observations of the kind described above give its thickness as only a few hundred miles. The photosphere is therefore a very thin skin round the sun. No wonder then that the limb is not blurred as we might expect the surface of a glowing ball of gas to be. (We have seen that this brilliant "skin" is in fact a seething mass of granules.)

The solar spectrum

We have stated earlier that light has two essential characteristics: intensity and color. The intensity can be deduced from the heating effect, or from the effect on a photoelectric cell. The problem of color is more diffi-

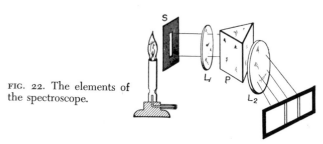

FIG. 22. The elements of
the spectroscope.

cult. The physicist, unlike the layman, does not look upon color as a mere sense impression on the retina. He knows that the eye cannot tell whether green light is a mixture of blue and yellow light or whether it comes from a green source. Furthermore, the eye is deceived by surrounding colors. In physics, therefore, light is characterized by its wave length or by its frequency, for light, just like a radio wave, must be considered an electromagnetic oscillation. The wave length of light is of the order of hundred millionths of centimeters and is measured in Ångström units. Each wave length corresponds to a certain color. Thus pure green light is of wave length 5500 A. (Ångström) units (i.e., 0.000055 cm). On the other hand apparently green light may have a different wave length since it may be a mixture of blue light (4500 A.) and yellow light (5900 A.).

The spectroscope

Physicists analyze light by means of the spectroscope (Fig. 22). The light from a given source, for instance from an electric lamp or from a flame, is passed through a slit S, and is focused on a screen by the two lenses L_1 and L_2. Without the prism P, the screen (just like the view-finder of a reflex camera) would show a sharp white image of the slit. The prism bends the rays in such a way that a colored spectrum, ranging from blue, through green and yellow, to red is thrown on the screen.

All light is bent to a characteristic degree, blue light being bent most and red light least. Every region on the screen thus corresponds to a certain wave length, no matter whether the light comes from an electric lamp, the sun, or a star.

Each chemical element has a characteristic spectral line

If, instead of using an electric lamp, we use a gas discharge tube (such as a neon sign) the spectrum on the screen will no longer be a continuous band of color ranging from 4000 A. in the blue to 7000 A. in the red. Instead, a number of bright lines, each a colored image of the slit, will appear in characteristic places on the screen. These spectral lines are emitted by the neon atoms in the tube. The strongest lines have the wave lengths 6402 A. (red) and 5862 A. (yellow). Other elements, such as hydrogen, nitrogen, or oxygen, produce other, characteristic, lines. Thus, the atoms of the elements may be likened to radio transmitters of different wave lengths. Just as the dial of a radio tells us what station we are receiving, so the screen of his spectroscope tells the physicist what atoms are responsible for the emission of particular lines. This applies equally to fluorescent tubes, to stars, or to the sun. The physical interpretation of this emission of discrete wave lengths or lines was, by the way, one of the greatest achievements of twentieth-century theoretical physics. The Danish physicist Niels Bohr, in laying the foundations of this new branch of atomic physics, opened the way to rapid developments, particularly in the field of astrophysics.

We have seen that an electric lamp—a glowing tungsten filament—gives a continuous, that is lineless, spectrum, while rarefied neon in a fluorescent tube produces a line spectrum. This difference is very important, and must be explained. While the neon atoms can move about freely in the tube and can therefore emit their characteristic wave lengths, the tungsten atoms in the filament cannot. Like the atoms of all solid or liquid materials, the tungsten atoms are packed so tight that their free emission of light is impeded. As a result their characteristic wave lengths overlap and become blurred, and thus we have a continuous spectrum. The distribution of energy in this spectrum gives the temperature of the radiant body, in this case the tungsten filament, but not its chemical composition.

The Fraunhofer spectrum

If we point a spectroscope at the sun, we obtain quite a different type of spectrum. While the neon tube gave us colored lines on a dark background, the sun produces dark lines on a colored background—a colored band interspersed with countless dark lines. Figure 23 shows a highly magnified section of the green part of the solar spectrum. On the same scale the entire solar spectrum from the blue to the red would be a few yards long.

The dark lines are best explained by an experiment. Let us place an electric lamp in front of the gas flame (Fig. 22) and sprinkle some salt on the flame. The salt turns the flame a brilliant yellow, but its brightness is still exceeded by that of the electric lamp. Two dark lines now appear on the yellow part of the spectrum in the same place, by the way, in which such dark lines appear in the solar spectrum also. Now, atoms not only emit, but also absorb radiation of exactly the same wave length, just as an aerial tuned to a certain wave length can emit and also receive this (and only this) wave length. The sodium atoms from the cooking salt

FIG. 23. Section of Fraunhofer spectrum in green light.

(sodium chloride) which we sprinkled on the gas flame evaporate and absorb the exact wave length in the continuous spectrum of the electric lamp which they themselves can emit. The black lines in the spectrum therefore represent the absence of these wave lengths. The absorbed light must, however, be re-emitted by the sodium atoms. If this were not so these atoms would be storing up an ever-increasing amount of light energy. But, while the absorbed light comes from only one direction—from the electric lamp—the re-emitted light is scattered in all directions. While no light is thus "lost," only a small part of it reaches the slit of the spectroscope. Hence the dark lines are not absolutely black.

The dark lines in the solar spectrum—called Fraunhofer lines after their discoverer (1814)—arise in a very similar way. The deep, hot, layers of the sun emit a continuous spectrum similar to that emitted by the electric lamp. In the outer, cooler, and more volatile regions of the sun (the photosphere corresponding to the gas flame in our experiment) part of this light is absorbed by the atoms there and scattered in all directions. The black lines in the solar spectrum are thus a good indication of the chemical elements present in the solar atmosphere.

The Fraunhofer spectrum of the sun has roughly 20,000 dark lines. The wave length of every line has been measured to within at least six significant figures, and all the lines have been classified during the last century. Thus the main yellow line of sodium is known to have the wave length 5895.932 A. Much painstaking work has enabled physicists to interpret more than 60 per cent of these lines, and so to derive a great deal of information about the distribution of chemical elements in the photosphere. Quite apart from that, the intensity and form of the lines give us valuable data about the temperature, the motion, and the density of the absorbing atoms in the solar atmosphere. The solar spec-

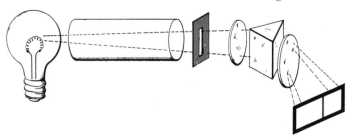

FIG. 24. Chemical analysis using the spectroscope.

trum with its 20,000 lines can therefore be likened to a telephone directory of a large town.

The chemical composition of the sun

From the lines, we can tell which of the 92 chemical elements are present in the solar atmosphere. Only a few are not, and their absence is probably due to the fact that their lines fall in a spectral region which, because of absorption by the terrestrial atmosphere, cannot be observed. Most light of wave lengths shorter than 2900 A. is absorbed by ozone and oxygen in the very high layers of our atmosphere.

The quantitative chemical analysis of the solar atmosphere, or of the atmosphere of any other star, is a very much more difficult problem than its qualitative analysis, the intensity of a given line not being a measure of the abundance of the corresponding element. The intensity of the line depends largely on the optical properties of the absorbing atoms also.

The intensity is determined in the following way: a tube (Fig. 24) is filled with a given gas, and, with a spectroscope, variations in the intensity of the absorption lines are compared with the quantity of gas used. The result is the so-called curve of growth, and by obtaining such curves for every element, the density of the absorbing atoms can be evaluated from the intensity of their lines. The curves of growth of most elements have now been calculated theoretically, and we know that the sun, like most other stars, consists largely of hydrogen. Hydrogen exists in roughly ten times the proportion of helium, and roughly a thousand times the proportion of carbon, nitrogen, or oxygen. The heavier the atoms, the rarer they are. Apart from hydrogen and helium, the chemical composition of the earth's crust, of the solar atmosphere, of the atmosphere of the stars, and of meteorites is roughly the same.

Even cosmic radiation which rains down on us from outer space with the velocity of light (186,000 miles per second) appears to have a similar composition of atomic nuclei. Thus, all known space seems to have a fairly even mixture of elements, and it is unlikely that any process can much affect this mixture. The present distribution of elements must therefore be as old as the universe itself.

v. *Solar Tower Telescopes*

Only sixty years ago, solar phenomena were still being observed by means of fairly small telescopes. Today, the solar physicist's equipment has become so bulky and complicated that it can no longer be moved to follow the sun's apparent motion in the sky. For this reason the sunlight must first be captured by a system of movable mirrors and then thrown on a fixed telescope.

Figure 25 shows a two-mirror system of this type, called the coelostat. The lower mirror—only its metal frame shows in the photograph—is carried on an axis which rotates once in 48 hours. (The reflected rays turn through twice the angle described by the rotating mirror.) This mirror throws the sunlight on another mirror (called the second-flat) so adjusted as to reflect the rays into the telescope. The mirrors have a diameter of 60 cm, and they are coated with aluminum so that the incident light is not refracted by the glass. To preserve the reflecting surfaces against the combined effects of sunlight and rotation, the mirrors are made very thick.

A modern coelostat is usually housed in a tower covered by a movable dome open to the sky on one side only. The rays are reflected down the tower by the second flat mirror. Because of the height of the tower, the coelostat is removed from the dangerous proximity of the ground, where thermal air militates against sharp definition.

Figure 26 is a diagrammatic sketch of the Einstein Tower built in Potsdam in 1919. The coelostat is mounted on a wooden scaffolding and both are protected from wind vibration by the outer structure and the dome. Internal vibrations are not communicated to the scaffolding since it stands on separate foundations. The rays are turned through 90° by a third mirror housed in a special well and thrown horizontally into a spectrograph room.

The tower at Mount Wilson, near Pasadena, California, is constructed in a somewhat different, very ingenious way. This tower is the first and largest solar tower in the world. It consists of two 150–foot high structural steel towers one inside the other. (The internal structure which carries the optical parts cannot be seen in Fig. 27.) The outer structure carrying the dome provides protection against the wind and helps

FIG. 25. Coelostat (Mt. Wilson Observatory).

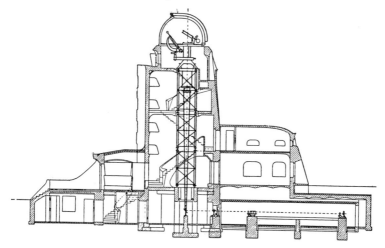

FIG. 26. Einstein Tower in Potsdam.

to achieve thermal stability. In this tower, the spectrograph is housed in a circular well 75 feet immediately beneath the tower. The telescope is directly below the coelostat, has a focal length of 150 feet and gives an image 16 inches in diameter. The movements of mirror and dome can be controlled from the laboratory, and the instruments can be reached by an external elevator.

During the last few years the number of solar towers has grown rapidly throughout the world. A replica of the Potsdam tower is found as far afield as Tokyo.

Solar spectrographs

Solar towers and coelostats obviate the motion of large instruments and thus remove restrictions on their size and weight. This applies particularly to the spectrographs used for analyzing sunlight. Many of these instruments are now larger and heavier than the telescopes which are used with them. Solar spectrographs have been greatly modified during recent years. The constant aim of the modifications was always to receive a

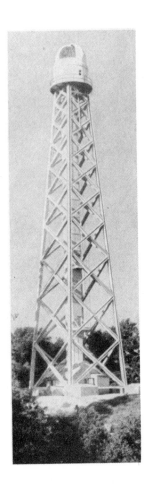

FIG. 27. Hale's solar tower on
Mt. Wilson.

maximum of incident light and to increase the resolving
power. More light is received when less light is wasted
through having to travel to the eye of an observer or
to a photographic plate. The resolving power of the
spectrograph is the ability of the instrument to separate
two wave lengths which are very nearly equal. This
ability is called the spectroscopic resolving power and is
the ratio of wave lengths to limiting difference of de-

tectable wave length $= \lambda/\Delta\lambda$. Compared once again to a telephone directory, the total number of data the spectrum supplies would correspond to the number of possible telephone connections.

In the older type of spectrograph the resolving power was largely determined by the size of the prism. Now, the larger a prism, the more prohibitive its cost. For this reason, prisms are increasingly being replaced by the so-called diffraction gratings. Diffraction gratings usually consist of a large number of equidistant parallel lines (usually about 15,000 lines an inch) ruled with a diamond point on glass or speculum metal. White light is diffracted according to its wave length, that is, it is separated into a colored band—a spectrum. The resolving power of the grating is determined by the total number of its lines, and the greater their number the more detailed the spectrum will be. The largest modern gratings are 10 inches square and have a total of about 150,000 lines.

A grating instead of producing only *one* spectrum gives a number of partly overlapping spectra. The greater the angle through which the incident light is turned by the grating, the less intense, but the more definite, are the spectral lines. The disadvantage of diminished intensity was recently remedied by the introduction of blazed gratings which are so ruled that the reflected light is concentrated into a few or even a single order of the spectrum. Because of their remarkable properties, blazed gratings are slowly replacing all others.

Resolving power is also increased by the use of interferometers which give a particularly good definition of small spectral regions—for example, a narrow spectral line. Further improvements were achieved by placing the entire spectrograph in an evacuated chamber, thus reducing the thermal effects of the air surrounding the spectrograph.

VI. *Eclipses of the Sun*

Paradoxically enough, our knowledge of the solar atmosphere is basically due to solar eclipses—to those few minutes during which the sun's disk is completely blotted out by the shadow of the moon.

More than four thousand years ago, on October 22 in the year 2137 B.C., a total eclipse of the sun occurred in China. The two royal astronomers, Hsi and Ho, having spent the day in merrymaking, were too far gone to carry out the customary rites and failed to shoot an arrow at the dragon which was about to swallow the sun. No wonder that the Emperor Chung K'ang had both of them beheaded. Warned by the tragic fate of Hsi and Ho, astronomers have ever since been careful to study solar eclipses with sobriety and diligence. Carrying their instruments halfway round the earth, they wait patiently for a few brief moments of darkness.

During an eclipse of the sun, the moon, in its orbit about the earth, blocks the light from the sun, thus creating darkness in the middle of the day (see Fig. 28).

Luckily enough, the moon happens to be just far enough to appear equal in size to the sun, and thus to cover it, at least during some eclipses. Needless to say, a total eclipse can only be observed over very small

FIG. 28. A total eclipse.

areas at any one moment—a circle of about 30 miles diameter. Within that circle, the sun is completely blotted out, and the stars appear in an otherwise dark sky. Since the moon, the earth, and the sun constantly shift their relative positions in space, this spectacle lasts for only a few minutes. Under favorable conditions, the moon's shadow can be seen to travel across the earth with very great speed. On June 30, 1954, the inhabitants of the Baltic island of Gotland, watching an eclipse from a promontory on the southern tip of the island, saw the amazing spectacle of a line dividing day from night traveling across the sea with incredible speed.

Outside the circle of complete darkness only a part of the sun appears covered by the moon, and we see a partial eclipse.

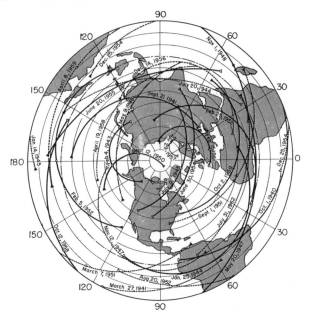

FIG. 29. Oppolzer's *Canon der Finsternisse.*

As the earth's orbit about the sun and the moon's orbit about the earth are known, solar eclipses—the time when sun, moon, and earth form a straight line in space —can be worked out very accurately. But even long before these orbits had been determined, the ancients had already managed to predict solar eclipses fairly accurately. The Chaldeans, the Egyptians, and the Greeks based their predictions on the observed periodicity of eclipses, particularly on the so-called *Saros* period of 18 years and $11\frac{1}{3}$ days. Nowadays, solar eclipses are predicted to the second through the co-operation of astronomers the world over. The time of arrival of an eclipse is also a useful tool for checking our knowledge of the terrestrial and lunar orbits.

Figure 29 is a map of solar eclipses between 1940 and 1962. It is taken from Oppolzer's famous *Canon der*

Finsternisse which predicted 8000 solar eclipses and 5200 lunar eclipses between 1208 B.C. and 2000 A.D. The dotted lines represent the path of the moon's shadow as it travels across the earth within a few hours. Many of these lines span an entire hemisphere. Eclipses occur almost every year, though most take place in regions too remote or else last for too short a time to be of any real use to astronomers. Often the moon does not cover the entire disk, and we have annular eclipses, which are of little help to the investigators. Most astronomers will have to go very far afield to observe future eclipses, since few will occur in inhabited regions.

We shall now examine the three distinct phases of a solar eclipse: the partial phase, lasting from the beginning of the eclipse until the disappearance of the sun, the few seconds between the disappearance of the sun and the appearance of the solar corona, and the total eclipse during which the corona is visible for a few minutes. The partial phase does not greatly concern solar astronomy, but is of great interest to radio astronomy and ionospheric physics.

The flash spectrum

When the moon has just about covered the solar disk, the outer layers of the photosphere appear as a very small sliver of light on one side of the limb. If the spectroscope is directed at this sliver just before totality, the dark lines of the Fraunhofer spectrum suddenly disappear and in their stead we now have a spectrum with colored lines on a dark background. This spectrum is known as the flash spectrum. Needless to say, it is emitted at all times and represents that light which is absent in the Fraunhofer lines and which, like the light of the sodium flame (Fig. 22) is normally scattered in all directions. For that reason this light is normally lost in the intense glare of the sun, just as the stars are. The sliver of light is so narrow that it acts as a spectrograph

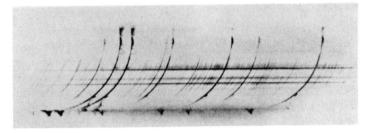

FIG. 30. Flash spectrum.

slit. Hence the spectrograph need consist of only a prism or diffraction grating and a photographic camera.

Spectra obtained in this way have curved spectral lines corresponding to the curvature of the "slit." Figure 30 shows that the lines are of different lengths, the long lines corresponding to a thick layer and the short lines to a thin layer of the sun. Astronomers therefore believed that some chemical elements might extend higher than others in the solar atmosphere. However, a careful comparison of the many data obtained during eclipses with other data has shown that the chemical composition is the same in all regions of the sun but that some of the atoms in the outer, hotter parts of the solar atmosphere have lost some of their electrons. Chemically speaking, they have not changed; they have merely become ionized to emit different spectral lines.

The appearance of the chromosphere

The chromosphere which emits the colored flash spectrum is some 6000 miles high and consists of much more highly rarefied gases than the photosphere. Figure 31 shows the appearance of the chromosphere at the instant before totality. The mountains of the moon can be seen below the bright chromosphere which, in turn, lies below the dark sky. On this photograph, the radius of the sun would be 20 inches. The structure of the chromosphere is far from uniform, and the famous Italian astronomer, Father Angelo Secchi, has compared this region to a burning prairie. Flames seem to be leaping up from it constantly. The larger flames are called spicules (spears), and each spicule is a mass of hot gases which, within a few minutes, shoots up to a height of 6000 miles with a speed of more than 18 miles per second.

The chromosphere is the "spray" of the photosphere

Unlike the terrestrial atmosphere, the chromosphere must be considered an ever-changing mass of gigantic breakers intermingling at supersonic speed. No doubt, like all supersonic effects, these phenomena in the chromosphere (and also those in the photosphere with its fast-rising granules) are accompanied by deafening noises.

The chromosphere has $1/1000$ to $1/10,000$ the density of the photosphere whose own density is about 10^{-8} g/cm^3. In other words, the mass of the chromosphere is very small compared with that of the photosphere. The chromosphere must be looked upon as being the spray of the heaving photosphere with its constantly rising whirlpools of granules. Just as the spray of the ocean swell has a much greater velocity than the heavy waves, so this spray of the chromosphere moves much faster

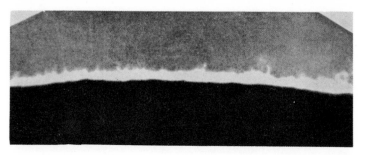

FIG. 31. Chromosphere over limb, shortly before totality.

than the convection currents in the denser photosphere.

Nowadays, it is possible to observe the chromosphere even at normal times—that is, apart from eclipses of the sun. In this way it was found that the matter ejected by the chromosphere is by no means thrown up arbitrarily, but that its motion is governed by the magnetic field of the sun (see Chapter VII).

So far, we have only spoken of the chromosphere as a phenomenon of the limb. Can we also obtain a picture of it against the disk, i.e. vertically? Clearly, this is not an easy task, since the chromosphere is practically transparent, and since its light is almost negligible when

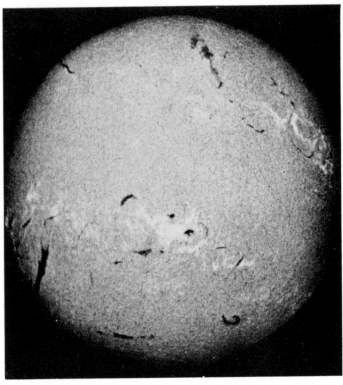

FIG. 32. Chromosphere seen against the disk on August 6, 1956 (Photograph: Fraunhofer Institute, Capri).

compared with that of the photosphere below it. Nevertheless, this difficult task has been accomplished and Figures 32 and 52 show the results.

The chief problem is the construction of a three-dimensional picture of the chromosphere from observations obtained at the disk and at the limb. The difficulty is that the disk picture (called the spectroheliogram) takes in only a certain depth, while limb photographs take in the entire depth. Only through the combination of direct observations, photographs, spectroheliograms, and detailed spectroscopic studies can one hope to get a complete picture of the chromosphere, its structure, its motion, its temperature, and the density of its gases. All the complicated facts involved are not yet fully understood, but roughly speaking this is what happens: as the rapidly rising photospheric granules rain incessant blows against the bottom of the chromosphere, they impart a large part of their kinetic energy to the chromosphere, in which, as a consequence, a system of spicules is formed. We shall see later that this transfer of energy by means of blows, or, more precisely, by shock waves, is also communicated to the corona, on which it has considerable heating effects. In fact, without this constant bombardment, there would probably be no solar corona at all.

Total eclipses

The chromosphere disappears as quickly as it came, to give way to utter darkness. No matter how much he knows about eclipses, the actual event will always fill the privileged observer with awed astonishment. We need hardly doubt the traditional story that having been at war with each other for five years, the Lydians and Medes laid down their arms after the total eclipse of May 17, 603 B.C., in deference to this sign from the heavens. They did so even though Thales is said to have forecast the eclipse well in advance.

The moment the moon covers the entire disk, the

FIG. 33. Solar corona on February 25, 1952 (Photograph: G. van Biesbroeck).

solar corona begins to glow, first as a luminous ring, then as a white, almost metallic, crown of light stretching far into space. The total brightness of the corona, which, during the few moments of totality dominates the whole sky, is only one millionth the normal brightness of the sun—it is about as bright as the full moon. (After a few seconds, once the eye has grown accustomed to the darkness, stars can be observed near the corona.) This explains why the solar corona cannot normally be seen through the dazzling light of the sun. Nevertheless, it is now possible by means of an ingenious optical instrument, the coronagraph, to detect the inner and brightest part of the solar corona even without an eclipse.

FIG. 34. Corona near sunspot minimum (top) and near sunspot maximum (bottom).

The corona

In the past 100 years, serious scientific investigations of the corona have been made during eclipses lasting altogether 100 minutes. Countless expeditions have been sent halfway round the world, simply to catch, say, five minutes of solar darkness in Java, two and a half minutes in Sweden, or four minutes in Brazil. Laboriously, scientists have collated what information we have about the sun's strange crown of light. While a great deal is already known, the corona has remained full of riddles, and for that very reason one of the solar astronomer's greatest challenges.

The corona assumes a different form with every eclipse, its form being closely associated with the sunspot cycle (Fig. 34). At maximum phase (many sunspots), streamers from the corona go out in all directions (maximum type). At minimum phase (few spots) on the other hand, the corona has large lateral streamers with small streamers in the polar regions (minimum type).

Figure 35 is a drawing of a minimum-type corona based on original photographs. The drawing must be thought of as having depth. The many prominences (see p. 111) near the limb have a shape that fits noticeably into the corona's curves and streamers. This is one strik-

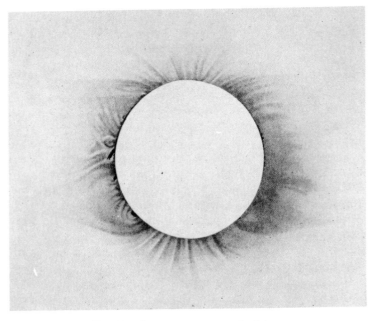

FIG. 35. Drawing of corona near sunspot minimum.

ing demonstration that the corona and the prominences are related as closely as, for instance, clouds are related to the terrestrial atmosphere.

Advances in spectroscopy and atomic theory during the last fifty years have gone a long way toward explaining the composition of the corona. It emits a continuous spectrum with roughly the same energy distribution as the solar spectrum. Only the dark lines are missing, and in their stead, but not their place, there are 20 bright emission lines. While the continuous spectrum was long ago interpreted as being due to the scattering of sunlight by the free electrons in the corona (this happens in roughly the same way that light is scattered by dust), the interpretation of the bright lines presented great difficulties. At first the lines were attributed to a new element not found on earth—coronium. However, the Swedish physicist Edlén managed to show that these lines appear when ordinary atoms such as calcium, iron, nickel and argon have a large number of planetary electrons torn off through ionization. Less extensive ionization phenomena are produced in the laboratory when an electric spark is sent through a rarefied gas. The corona, therefore, is made up of gases that chemically, apart from free electrons, are almost the same as those of the rest of the sun. The strong ionization of the atoms indicates that the gases in the corona are at a very high temperature. Many other observations also go to show that the coronal temperature is about 1,000,000°. This sounds frightening since, were the corona to have the same mass as the rest of the sun, the intense radiation associated with so high a temperature would quickly put an end to all life on earth. Fortunately, the gases in the corona are highly rarefied, and the density of even the innermost, densest parts is only 10^{-11} of the density of the terrestrial atmosphere at ground level. Thus, the energy radiated by the corona is insignificant in comparison with the rest of solar radiation.

The gaseous particles in the corona fly about with great speeds (protons at about 125 miles per second and electrons at about 5000 miles per second) and collide with one another violently enough for many of their electrons to be wrenched off. The corona stretches far into space, probably much further than the eye can see during the brief minutes of a total eclipse. We shall see that the corona's outermost branches occasionally reach the earth where they have a demonstrable effect on the magnetic field.

The reader might be surprised that the gas in the corona has a temperature of 1,000,000° when the surface of the sun below it has a temperature of at most 10,000°. Unfortunately, no complete explanation has yet been given, but it is believed that, just as the photosphere heats the chromosphere by thrusting up its granules, so the chromosphere heats the corona by means of its supersonic spray. In reality the boundaries between photosphere, chromosphere, and corona are not as definite as we have made them appear. The quantitative interpretation of the energy exchanges between the different strata of the solar atmosphere is still incomplete, since the exchanges are effected by supersonic shock waves arising under conditions that cannot be repeated experimentally, for example, in wind tunnels. To make matters even more difficult, magnetic fields and the electric properties of the gases in the corona must be taken into consideration. It is for these reasons that the corona has retained some of its mysterious character.

Observations of the corona without an eclipse

The invention of the coronagraph by the French astronomer, Bernard Lyot, was a milestone in research on the corona. By means of the coronagraph the inner parts of the corona can now be observed without an eclipse.

We have seen that the corona is roughly as bright as the full moon, that is, its brightness is a millionth that of the sun. Many astronomers had vainly tried to observe the weak light of the corona against the bright disk. The main difficulty was the presence of an intense brightness around the sun. This is produced when sunlight is scattered by dust in our own atmosphere. Only on high mountains are these scattering effects minimized. This had been known even before Lyot's invention, but astronomers had overlooked the scattering effects produced in the telescope itself. Now, the telescope objective receives light from the entire sun, and the smallest scratch or dust particle on it will therefore scatter more sunlight than the total light received from the corona. Lyot was the first to realize this and to draw the necessary conclusions. In the summer of 1930 he took his newly invented instrument up to the Pic du Midi observatory in the Pyrenees, and managed to observe the corona with it. His telescope was based on a very simple principle. The objective A of highly polished crown glass, selected for freedom from internal blemishes, throws the sun's image on a reflecting metal cone B, which intercepts the direct light of the disk so that the corona itself can be seen (Fig. 36).

In addition, a small opaque spot at D intercepts the small image of the sun formed by double reflection from the surfaces of the objective A which is focused on D by the field lens C. The coronagraph enables astronomers to view the solar corona during about 150 to 200 days of the year. Its structure can be studied and the

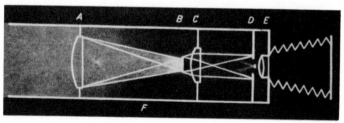

FIG. 36. The coronagraph.

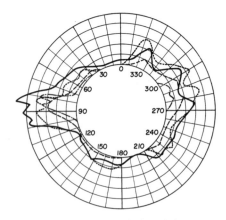

FIG. 37. Comparative coronal contours in the light of the green coronal line. —— Pic du Midi, ... Arosa, - - - - Wendelstein (Bavaria), –·–· Zugspitze.

intensity of the coronal emission lines measured right round the disk.

Since the coronagraph serves only for observations on the limb, the total picture over the entire disk must be compounded from a host of individual observations. For this reason, the solar corona is currently observed from coronagraphs stationed in different parts of the world, and the data obtained are collated internationally. The seven stations are: the Pic du Midi (9469 ft., in France), Arosa (6725 ft., in Switzerland), Wendelstein (6035 ft., in Bavaria), Kanzelhöhe (6230 ft., in Austria), Climax (10,480 ft., in Colorado), Sacramento Peak (9050 ft., in New Mexico), and Mount Norikura (9510 ft., in Japan).

Figure 37 is a set of polar diagrams of coronal intensities taken simultaneously at different stations. The contours do not represent the shape of the corona, the distances from the limb corresponding to the intensity of the green line 5303 A. at a fixed point. This spectral line, known as FeXIV, is emitted by an iron atom that has lost thirteen of its shell electrons through ionization. We shall have to return to this line on p. 126, where we shall learn that fluctuations in coronal intensities are closely associated with sunspots and prominences, and that the photosphere, the chromosphere, and the corona are related in much the same way as are the earth, the ocean, and the terrestrial atmosphere.

Before his death in 1952 Lyot had greatly improved coronal observations. The corona is no longer observed visually or photographically, but its light is made to impinge upon a photoelectric cell which transforms the light into measureable electric currents. Used in connection with special amplifiers, these cells enable one to detect differences in brightness, even though these differences may be very small when compared with the total intensity. This electronic procedure is used in many branches of physics and astronomy, particularly in radio astronomy, in measurements of the magnetic field of the sun, and in evaluating the polarization of light from distant stars. This does not mean, however, that visual observations and the time-honored photographic plate, have been completely discarded. In solar observations, particularly, the human eye continues to play a paramount role, and, though the photographic plate is not nearly as sensitive as the photoelectric cell, it has an inestimable advantage: it produces a picture of a surface, whereas the photoelectric cell can only measure the brightness of a succession of single points.

VII. *The Changing Face of the Sun*

The sun is a glowing ball of gas of diameter 864,000 miles. It is held together by gravitational forces, and its diameter is unlikely to have changed a great deal in billions of years. In all probability the sun will retain its shape for billions of years to come. Nevertheless, many comparatively small changes do take place on and in the sun. Surface changes are no doubt similar to surface changes on countless other stars, where they cannot be observed, since even the nearest stars remain mere points of light in even the largest telescopes. Thus, although we observe the light of the stars, neither their shape nor the way the light is distributed over their surface can be determined. Solar physics, therefore, plays a very special role in astrophysics—by investigating the details of one star, it acts as guide to stellar research in general.

The number of observable solar events—or phenomena—is very large indeed. The phenomena are all interrelated in roughly the same way that meteorological processes on earth combine to make up our weather conditions. For this reason, we may call the corresponding solar phenomena the "solar weather."

The discovery of sunspots

The oldest known of these phenomena are the sunspots. Normally, sunspots cannot be detected with the naked eye, but when the light of the sun is sufficiently weakened by mist, fog, thin clouds, or reddening at dusk, larger groups of sunspots, whose diameter may be as much as one-tenth the solar diameter, can be made out.

The real discovery of sunspots dates from the invention of the telescope, though sunspots are mentioned in older reports. At the time, no one paid much attention to these reports, people dismissing them as optical illusions or fantasies. Small wonder then that when Johannes Fabricius saw sunspots through the recently invented telescope in December 1610, he was taken completely by surprise. His discovery is reported in his *Narratio de maculis in sole observatis et apparente earum cum sole conversione* (Wittenberg, 1611), where we can read:

"I directed the telescope at the sun. It appeared to have a variety of inequalities and flaws. While I was observing these carefully, I was unexpectedly shown a black spot whose magnitude compared with the body of the sun was not inconsiderable. I then thought that passing clouds were responsible for the spot. I repeated the observation some ten times with Batavian telescopes of different sizes until I was finally convinced: clouds could not have caused these spots. Not believing my own eyes, I hastened to call my father. Both of us then caught the sun's rays in a telescope, first on the limb, then, as we moved the telescope slowly towards the center and as our eyes became accustomed to the rays, over the entire disk. Then we saw the object of our search more clearly and certainly. Thus passed the first day, and our curiosity oppressed our night, as we lay wondering whether the spot was truly on the sun or beyond it. . . . Next morning, to my great joy, I found the spot again straight away. However the spot seemed to have changed its position a little, which caused us some anxiety. . . . Now the sky was overcast for three days. When it cleared once again, the spot had travelled from east to west. . . ."

Some months later Christoph Scheiner, a Jesuit father from the town of Ingolstadt, also saw spots on the sun, but was so severely taken to task by his superior for "claiming to have seen things of which nothing could be read in Aristotle" that he was afraid to make any further observations for six months. He then wrote to Galileo, who promptly replied that he himself had observed spots as early as August 1610. Galileo, however, had not appreciated the full importance of his discovery.

At first, opinions about the nature of sunspots differed. While some, to save the purity of the sun at all costs (the eye of the universe could not possibly be impaired), spoke of hitherto undiscovered planets (some called them the "Austrian planets" and the Frenchman Tarde called them the "Bourbon planets"), others saw the spots as the "slag" of the burning sun. This slag was periodically ejected by the sun in the form of comets, so that the sun could once more shine "like the light of a trimmed wick." Kepler, who also observed sunspots in 1613, believed them to be solar clouds which, since they did not move across the disk with uniform speed, and since they came and went, could not be part of the solar atmosphere. He thought that they were probably opaque clouds of smoke rising up from the white-hot sun.

The nature of the sunspots was understood much better by Father Christoph Scheiner. Using an equatorially mounted telescope he saw clearly that the spots turned with the sun. Having determined the period of the sun's rotation, he even noticed that sunspots changed their latitude in the course of the years.

Spots and the rotation of the sun

Modern telescopes reveal little more of the solar surface than Scheiner's telescope did 300 years ago. Figure 14 is a photograph of the sun taken in white light. On it we can see that the spots are grouped in two parallel

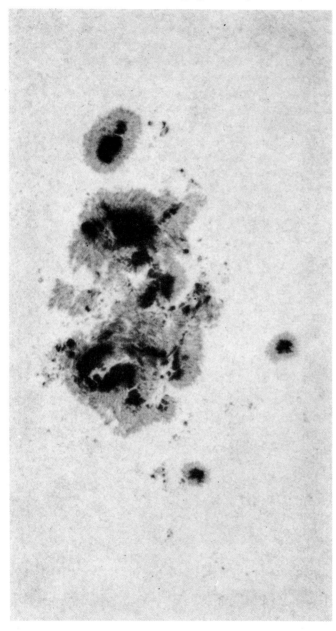

FIG. 38. Large group of sunspots. Note the granulation surrounding the group (Mt. Wilson Observatory).

zones north and south of the equator. The spots travel across the disk, taking roughly 13½ days to travel from east to west. More durable spots return to the eastern edge after a further interval of 13½ days. The sun therefore appears to rotate once in 27 days. Now, during that time, the earth itself has moved along its orbit about the sun. A more exact determination shows that the sun takes 25.4 days to rotate about its axis. This period is called the sidereal period of rotation, while that observed from the earth is known as the synodic. The sidereal period of rotation corresponds to an equatorial velocity of about 1¼ miles per second.

The sun's axis is inclined by about 7° to the plane of the earth's orbit, that is, to the ecliptic. Thus, the inclination of the sun's axis will appear to vary with the position of the earth on its orbit about the sun. Now, the position of the spots enables us to determine the true position of the sun's axis and thus to divide the sun into latitudes and longitudes—into heliographic coordinates (see Fig. 64).

Oddly enough, the sun's rotational velocity varies with heliographic latitude, the equator rotating faster than the polar caps. The sun does not rotate like a solid body, but twists on its axis. This constant twisting is probably not restricted to the surface alone, the differential rotation affecting the underlying strata also, so that vast interior areas of the sun become contorted. The resulting friction and currents are probably one of the causes of the many changeable surface phenomena.

Sunspots are cooler than the surrounding photosphere

What is a sunspot? Figure 38 shows that each spot consists of a dark nucleus called the umbra, and a border called the penumbra. Naturally, the umbra is not completely black, and only appears to be so in contrast to the very much brighter background. For this reason, details of the umbra can occasionally be picked out. The diameter of a spot can be anything between a few thousand miles (very roughly the diameter of the earth) and more than 30,000 miles. The darkness of the umbra must be associated with a considerable drop in temperature at that spot, the temperature here being some 1500° lower than in the surrounding photosphere, where it is about 6000°. It is difficult to explain this drop in temperature before a fuller discussion of the other physical properties of sunspots.

The life history of sunspots

Sunspots have a marked tendency to join together into groups. The life history of every group begins with the formation of a tiny spot due to the separation of photospheric granules and the consequent appearance of a dark "pore" between them. The pore is soon joined by other pores, and these small groups of pores or spots generally disappear after a few hours, but sometimes their development continues to follow the course shown in Figure 39.

The nine stages shown in this figure represent the nine classes A to I of the so-called Zurich classification. The penumbra first appears in type C and keeps growing until type F is reached. Large F groups can attain lengths of more than 125,000 miles, and contain up to 100 individual spots. Their maximum size is generally reached after about 10 days. A given group of spots will frequently reappear at the eastern edge of the disk 13½ days after it has disappeared behind the western edge. Only some exceptionally large groups of spots survive more than two rotations of the sun, though the most persistent group so far observed has managed to survive five rotations.

The number of visible sunspots is variable. As a measure of their frequency, R. Wolf of Zurich introduced his "relative sunspot number" in 1849. It is defined as $R = 10\,g + f$ where f is the number of individual spots

A

B

C

D

E

F

G

H

I

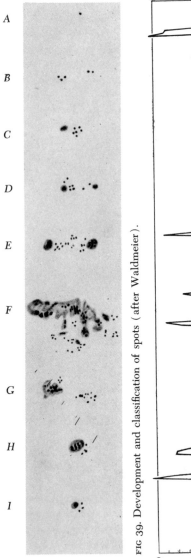

FIG 39. Development and classification of spots (after Waldmeier).

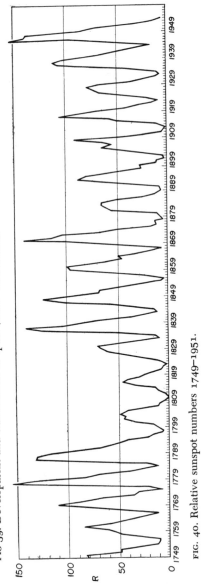

FIG. 40. Relative sunspot numbers 1749–1951.

and g the number of groups. The sunspot number on the disk shown in Figure 14 would therefore be given by $R = 10 \times 8 + 37$, since in this case g equals 8 groups and f equals 37 individual spots. This odd system is still in use even though it is very arbitrary. It must be emphasized that Wolf's sunspot number refers only to the spots on the side of the sun which we happen to be facing. Wolf's number, therefore, depends on the position of the earth relative to the sun and is not a true solar measure.

Figure 40 is a graph of sunspot numbers for the last 200 years, the figures for the eighteenth century having been compiled laboriously from a host of different sources. From the graph it would appear that the sun's sunspot activity is of a periodic nature. While the spots disappear almost completely for some months (sunspot minima), at other times (sunspot maxima) more than fifteen groups seem to cover the sun's face with freckles. A full cycle takes about eleven years, and the average interval between minimum and maximum (about 4.6 years) is smaller than the average interval between maximum and minimum (about 6.7 years). Even the heights of the maxima fluctuate considerably. Thus the height of the 1778 maximum was not equaled until 1947.

Are sunspots truly periodic?

It was previously believed that the sunspot cycle resulted from the superposition of different periodic cycles. Some astronomers maintained that these periods were associated with the motion of the planets, particularly with that of Jupiter, whose period is eleven years. Since then it has become quite clear that the rise and fall in the number of spots is due to a number of practically independent individual processes. Thus the idea of a true periodic phenomenon was dropped in favor of the so-called "eruption hypothesis." On this hypothesis, each

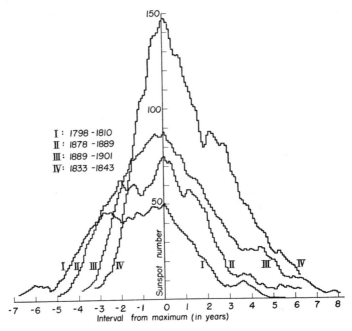

I : 1798 -1810
II : 1878 -1889
III : 1889 -1901
IV : 1833 -1843

FIG. 41. Typical spot curves (after Waldmeier).

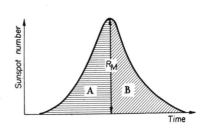

FIG. 42. Diagram representing a sunspot cycle.

cycle represents an independent eruption of the sun which takes about eleven years to die down. Figure 41 shows four such cycles—the cycles of 1798–1810, 1878–89, 1889–1901, and 1833–43. The horizontal axes represent the interval in years from the maximum. The curves have two special properties emphasizing the eruptive character of the cycles. This is best illustrated by a consideration of Figure 42. It was found that the area A is constant for all cycles, while the area B varies with the height of the sunspot maximum R_M. In other words, the more violent the cause, the faster the eruption, since, if all eruptions took place equally fast, the area A would also vary with R_M. Once the sunspot maximum is reached, the force of the eruption is spent. The area A is therefore a measure of the total energy that went into the explosion, while the area B might represent the total mass of lava ejected in, say, a terrestrial eruption. Unfortunately, this formal analogy between a sunspot cycle and an eruption is not yet understood in all its physical detail, the real mechanism being hidden in the interior of the sun. We can only speculate about it.

However, we can predict the course of any cycle once it has started from its characteristic eruption curve. This is important since sunspot activity affects the transmission of short radio waves over long distances (see p. 150).

The migration of sunspots

The assumption that sunspot fluctuations are not truly periodic, like the oscillations of a pendulum, becomes even more probable if, in addition to their frequency, we also consider their distribution over the disk. As we have seen, sunspots do not appear just anywhere but in two belts parallel to the solar equator. These belts tend to move toward the equator. The leading spot of an eleven-year cycle appears roughly in latitudes 30°N. or

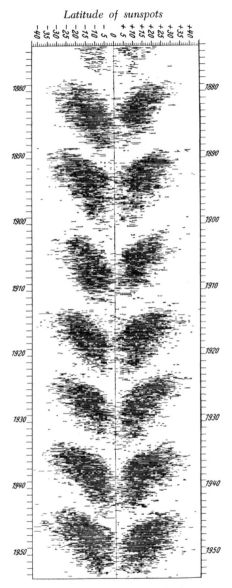

FIG. 43. "Butterfly" diagram representing the latitude distribution of sunspots (after H. W. Newton, Greenwich).

S. (where it persists for some weeks). The spot belts reach the latitudes 8°N. or S. at the end of that cycle. The regularity of this zonal migration is best illustrated by the famous Maunder's "butterfly diagram" which gives the position of all observed spots between 1874 and 1953 (Fig. 43). The vertical axis represents the time and the horizontal axis the North and South latitudes. This sunspot "map" not only emphasizes the regular shift of sunspot zones toward the equator in the course of a cycle, but shows even better than the eruption curve that individual cycles are independent. Each cycle is an isolated butterfly and does not touch its neighbor. The diagram tells us even more: while one cycle expires in the lower latitudes, the first spots of the new cycle are forming in the higher latitudes. The cycles therefore overlap, sometimes by as much as four years. This could not possibly occur in a purely periodic process. Even the shift in latitude is therefore determined by the violence of the internal eruption. The greater the sunspot activity, the higher the latitude in which the first spots of the cycle appear.

Sunspots are magnetic

More than 100 years ago, Sir Joseph Lockyer noticed that some of the spectral lines in the umbra are doubled. Only toward the turn of the century did the great American pioneer of solar research, George Ellery Hale, manage to give a physical interpretation of this phenomenon. Zeeman's previous discovery that atoms in a magnetic field can emit double lines led Hale to suspect the existence of magnetic fields in the chromosphere above a sunspot. Here the chromosphere frequently shows a vortex structure when observed in hydrogen light (see Fig. 57), and Hale believed that these vortices were a sign of electric currents which then produced magnetic fields. Today, we know that the magnetic field of the spots is a result of internal processes and that the visible vortices are a partial consequence of this magnetic field and not its cause. Even so, the confusion of cause and effect had led to a great discovery.

How can we tell the existence of magnetic fields from the solar spectrum? This is best explained by an account of Zeeman's original experiment. When a Geissler tube, specially designed to demonstrate the luminous effects of an electric discharge through a rarefied gas, was placed in the powerful magnetic field of an electromagnet, a sensitive spectrograph recorded a shift of spectral lines and, in the case of very strong magnetic fields, a splitting of the lines into two or more. This shift of spectral lines from their normal position enabled Zeeman to assess the strength of a distant magnetic field.

Unlike Zeeman's experimental spectrum, the sunspot spectrum consists of absorption and not of emission lines. Even so, their displacement from the normal position is also a measure of the intensity of the magnetic field in the sunspot. Figure 44 shows the spectrum of a spot. In the dark strip, representing the umbra, the Fraunhofer lines have clearly been shifted.

The fact that the shift is greatest in that region indicates that the magnetic field must be strongest here. However, other factors, for example, quick motions on the part of the light-emitting atoms, can also produce shifts in line. For this reason magnetic shifts had to be distinguished from all others. This is done by considering the polarization of the shifted components.

Some lines in the solar spectrum, particularly those emitted by iron atoms, are especially suited to measuring the intensity of magnetic fields. The results of systematic investigations over many years, most of them carried out at Mount Wilson Observatory in California, have shown that all sunspots have strong magnetic fields, the field intensity varying with the size of the spots. The intensity can increase to more than 3000

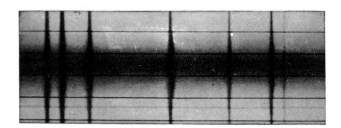

FIG. 44. Spectrum of a sunspot.

Gauss (the strength of the terrestrial magnetic field, which is responsible for turning a compass needle, is only about 0.2 Gauss).

Almost all groups of spots contain spots of opposite polarity and are therefore known as bipolar groups. Occasionally, when only one magnetic pole is present in a group, the (assumed) space of the other pole is represented by a weak magnetic field. Hale called this field an "invisible spot." A visible spot will generally appear in this field at a later date. The magnetic field would therefore seem to precede the formation of a spot and the consequent cooling of its umbra.

The magnetic cycle lasts 22 years

In 1913, Hale and his collaborators were very surprised to notice that the magnetic polarity of spots of a new cycle showed the reverse arrangement of that of the ending cycle. While previously the leading spot of a group rotating westward had been a North pole, now it was always a South pole. At the end of that particular cycle (1924), the polarity became reversed once again. Figure 45 illustrates the connection between the migration of zones, the spot activity, and this change in polarity. The reversal of polarity starts with the beginning of each new cycle—at the time of spot minima. Thus, two spot cycles, or roughly 22 years, go by before the original polarity is reached again, and hence two spot cycles must go into a complete solar cycle.

The regularity of this magnetic phenomenon is best seen from Figure 46 showing the respective polarity of the leading spot during the years 1922–25.

Exceptions are few, so that the magnetic behavior of sunspots literally brings to light—that is, to the surface—messages from the interior of the sun. From these messages we can deduce the existence of gigantic and regular currents in the interior of the sun.

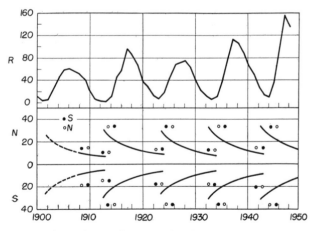

FIG. 45. Polarity law and spot cycle (bottom), sunspot number (top).

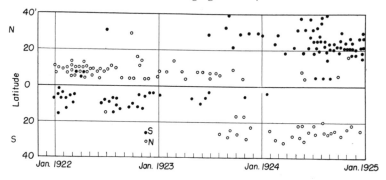

FIG. 46. Reversal of polarity of the "leading" spot in both parts of the solar hemisphere.

Solar electricity

Before we can understand the physical properties of sunspots, we must discuss the special characteristics of solar electric and magnetic phenomena. These characteristics cannot be demonstrated in the laboratory, and conclusions about the sun from experiments are therefore dangerous and have given rise to many misconceptions.

A magnetic field can be established either by a permanent magnet, for example, a horseshoe magnet made of magnetized steel, or by a nonferrous coil of copper wire carrying an electric current. In the case of the horseshoe magnet (ferromagnetism) the field is due to the fact that electrons revolve about individual atoms which are arranged like so many regular crystals. In the electromagnet, the electrons do not revolve about individual atomic nuclei, but are forced to revolve through regular windings of the coil. Basically, then, the two magnetic fields are established in very similar ways.

Ferromagnetism with its regular atoms cannot, of course, occur on the gaseous sun, and the magnetic fields associated with sunspots must therefore be due to large-scale electric currents, namely, currents produced by the motions of free electrons and positive ions.

Once an electric current on the sun has begun to flow, it keeps on flowing. This phenomenon can be demonstrated by an experiment. If a current is sent through a coil of wire, and the source of the current is suddenly turned off, the induced magnetic field will persist for a short time—the duration depending on the cross section of and resistance of the coil. Hence it follows that the current must also continue to flow for a short time. (The time varies directly with the cross section of the coil and inversely with the resistance of the wire.)

In a coil of diameter 10 cm the field lags behind by only some thousandths of a second. In a sunspot, however, we have a "coil" some 10,000 km in diameter—10^{16} times as thick as our experimental coil. More exact calculations show that the magnetic field in the solar "coil" will only die out a hundred years after the mechanism causing the current has been "switched off." The continued flow and the consequent persistence of the magnetic field are thus the direct result of the large dimensions of the spot and the relatively good electric conductivity of solar matter. Since the electric currents responsible for the persistence of the magnetic fields must flow through matter, and also since the electrons themselves must be constituents of that matter, magnetic fields and matter are inseparably related. The magnetic field is said to be "frozen into matter." When matter is in motion, its system of electric currents and the associated magnetic field are moved in almost the same way that a magnetic field moves when a horseshoe magnet is shifted.

Sunspots are magnetic refrigerators

Why does the temperature drop in the umbra of sunspots? Why does the umbra have a strong magnetic field? These questions continue to bother investigators to this day. A great number of very general theories has been put forward, many of which were based on sheer speculation. Now, experience has shown, and not in solar research alone, that such theories cannot stand up for long and that they generally break down the moment any new observation is made. The more realistic theories prefer to concentrate on one aspect of a problem alone and to make do with a minimum of hypotheses. In due course the partial results may then fit into a consistent whole.

A spot is darker than its environment. Strangely enough it is the spot and not the surrounding photosphere whose brightness must be called "normal." While the temperature and brightness of the photosphere are considerably raised above "normal" by the hydrogen convection currents (granulation is one of their visible results), the convection currents are damped in the umbra, in much the same way that a rotating copper disk is slowed down when it is introduced into a magnetic field. Once the convection is braked, therefore, the temperature does not rise further. Thus the lower temperature inside a spot is due to the presence of a magnetic field. This agrees with the observation that magnetic fields occasionally appear in the place of a future spot.

Magnetic fields are older than spots

We have seen that a magnetic field with the dimensions of a sunspot must have a lifetime of more than 100 years. Nevertheless, there are many spots which only last for hours or a few days. The obvious inference is that the magnetic fields associated with sunspots must have existed long before the appearance of the spot and that they will continue to exist long after their disappearance. Sunspots are therefore the visible manifestations of invisible processes in the solar interior.

Origin of the magnetic fields

If we measure the strength of the magnetic field in the center of a spot, we shall notice that it does not vary with the size of the spot. It rises rapidly shortly after the spot has formed, remains constant for a time, and drops rapidly shortly before the spot finally disappears. This observation is further evidence that the magnetic field exists before the appearance of the spot and that the spot simply draws our attention to its existence.

The origin of the magnetic field has been explained in different ways. While some astronomers suspect it to arise independently in the vicinity of a spot, others believe that the field in the spot is merely a local intensification of the general magnetic field of the sun. So far, the matter is undecided, though the independent origin theory is by far the simpler of the two. Since every magnetic field is associated with matter and since matter is subject to considerable fluctuations in movement and density, magnetic fields may well become "thinned out" or "thickened," that is, intensified. If we think of the sun as having a magnetic field like the earth, a compass on the sun would always point north. Now, we have seen that, unlike the earth, the sun does not rotate like a solid body, the solar equator rotating much more quickly than the poles. A rubber band laid along a meridian from the equator to the pole would eventually be stretched into a circle parallel to the equator, and so would the magnetic lines of force. Thus our compass needle would no longer point to the pole but come to lie parallel to the equator. Furthermore, local differences in rotation not only influence the form but also give rise to local intensifications of the field. The field can therefore be likened to the currents within a colored gas. Occasionally, the currents will cause a concentration of the gas at a given spot and thus an increase in color.

seems probable that the differential rotation is the cause of the magnetic fields in the spots and also of the drop in temperature. However, a great deal of research is still needed before this hypothesis can be considered to be fully established. It is by no means certain how deep within the sun this concentration takes place and how the resulting field comes to the surface as a spot. The field is probably thrown up by vortices resulting from the differential rotation. Since, however, these vortices occur below the surface and are invisible, one cannot be absolutely certain about the validity of this explanation. The surface vortices which spectro-heliograms often detect above sunspots (see Fig. 57) have little connection with these internal disturbances, and must rather be likened to storms in our own atmosphere.

The demonstrable effects of a general, and probably variable, magnetic field outside the spots and also the rotational deviations are so small that their detection seems almost impossible. Furthermore, the associated theoretical study of the behavior of ionized (electrically charged) gases in the sun's magnetic field is still in its infancy. This work, which has recently assumed great importance, is known as solar electrodynamics.

Even so, we have every reason to believe that the study of sunspots is moving on the right lines.

Optical sections through the solar atmosphere

Before discussing other variable solar phenomena, we must quickly examine the instruments used for looking at different slices of the solar atmosphere.

The normal telescope, which admits sunlight of all colors, shows only the photosphere, with its granules and sunspots. For examining the higher layers, solar physicists make use of a method discovered almost simultaneously by Hale and Deslandres about 1890. This method is based on the fact that the light from the photo-

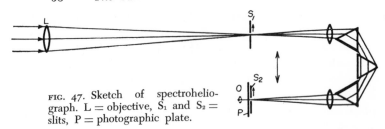

FIG. 47. Sketch of spectroheliograph. L = objective, S_1 and S_2 =
slits, P = photographic plate.

sphere passes unweakened through the higher layers of
the solar atmosphere except for certain wave lengths
which are absorbed to give rise to Fraunhofer lines.
A selective filter which only passes a given Fraunhofer
line would thus cut out light from the photosphere. The
darker a given line, that is, the greater the absorption,
the higher the region observed. By passing a chosen line
only, the filter can be thus used for "dissecting" the
solar atmosphere.

The spectroheliograph

This dissection is performed by the spectroheliograph
(Fig. 47), a spectrograph with a slit S_1 on which an
image of the sun is thrown by the lens L. The sunlight
is dispersed by a diffraction grating (see page 61). A
second slit S_2 selects the desired dark line from the
rest of the spectrum. A photographic plate O is placed
immediately behind the slit S_2. Now, if the entire
spectrograph is moved so that the slit S_1 passes across
the fixed image of the sun and the slit S_2 across the
photographic plate, the resulting photograph will be
taken in the light of the selected line only.

If the slice of the solar atmosphere is to be observed
directly, the slits S_1 and S_2 can be set into rapid oscillation, and the persistency of vision enables one to view
an image in the light of the chosen line. This instrument is called the spectrohelioscope.

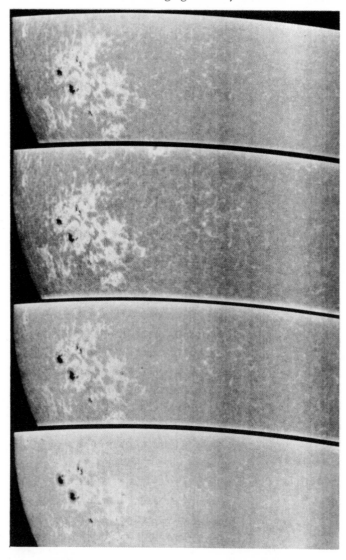

FIG. 48. Four spectroheliograms taken in calcium light. Highest level of sun (top), lowest level (bottom).

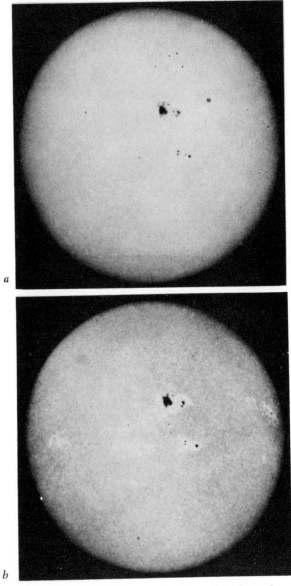

FIG. 49. Different levels of the solar atmosphere: (*a*) photosphere
(white light), (*b*) upper photosphere (K$_2$),

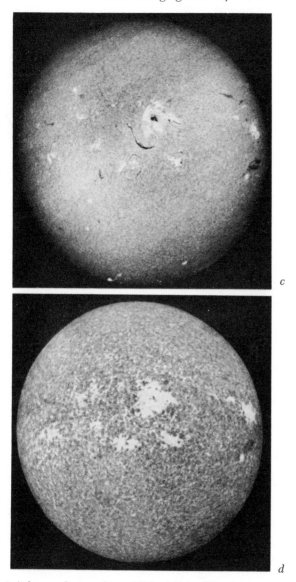

c

d

(*c*) lower chromosphere (Hα), (*d*) middle chromosphere (K₃).
(Photographs: Meudon and Fraunhofer Institute, Freiburg.)

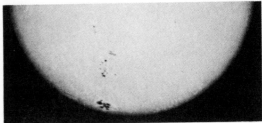

FIG. 50.
Faculae near the limb in white light (Fraunhofer Institute).

Faculae

Figure 48 shows four spectroheliograms taken in the light of the very intense and broad ultraviolet (just visible) line of ionized calcium. The top picture was taken exactly in the center of the line and the others increasingly toward the outer—the brighter parts—of the line. The top picture therefore shows the uppermost and the lowest picture the lowermost slice of the solar atmosphere. The differences are striking, the spots being clearest in the lower and covered by luminous clouds in the top picture. The photographs having been taken in the light of calcium, these clouds must be self-luminous calcium clouds with a temperature greater than that of the photosphere. Such clouds are known as faculae and are always found above and near sunspots. They often appear earlier than the spots and frequently survive them by weeks or even months. Faculae can also be found away from groups of spots, but such faculae are less bright and smaller. Seen in the light of other lines, that is, at different levels of the solar atmosphere, the faculae change their appearance. Thus, the faculae in the middle layer of the atmosphere (taken in the red line of hydrogen) look darker and less compact. These differences are clearly illustrated in the photographs of Figure 49, taken in different lines or different parts of the same line. While no faculae appear

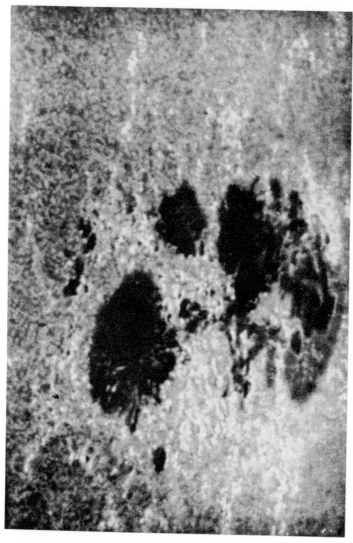

FIG. 51. Photospheric facular region near the limb in white light (Ten Bruggengate).

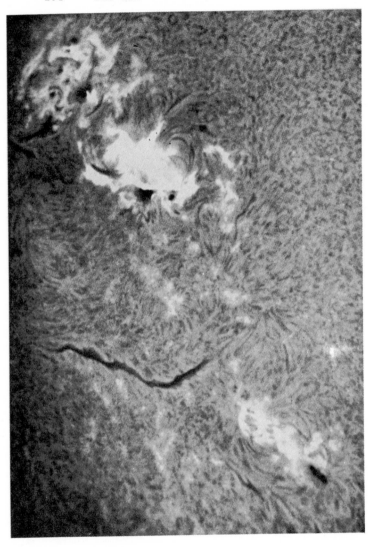

FIG. 52. Solar flare on November 7, 1956 (Lyot-filter photograph, Fraunhofer Institute, Capri).

on photograph (*a*) taken in white light, photograph
(*d*) of the uppermost layer (taken in the center of the
calcium line) is dominated by them.

Faculae can, however, be seen even in white light
also, but only near the limb, where the photosphere is
viewed obliquely and its own light sufficiently weakened. The white faculae seen at the limb have almost
the same characteristics as the faculae on other parts
of the disk.

Faculae are warning signals

All the observed faculae have a fine structure. While
this fine structure is not easily detected in the chromosphere (see Fig. 52), it appears clearly in the beady
structure of some photospheric faculae near the limb
(Fig. 51). Though the brightness of individual beads
fluctuates, the faculae as such do not change their form.

Faculae, however irregular their appearance, must
be considered as the outward signs of internal processes.
Their form and brightness are not only a measure of
the stage of development reached by the spots below
them, but also of the intensity of the primary factors
causing the spots to appear. Faculae are therefore warn-
ing signals of an impending disturbance in or below
the photosphere, and in many respects they give a more
reliable indication of the solar activity than even the
sunspots do. A number of observations indicate that
faculae are probably due to magnetic processes. If so,
we must take it that gas clouds are brought to white
heat by the appearance of variable magnetic fields. This
heating effect can be demonstrated in the laboratory,
although, of course, on a very much smaller scale. When
a glass tube containing a rarefied gas is introduced into
an alternating magnetic field—that is, a field due to a
coil carrying a high-frequency A.C. potential—the gas
becomes luminescent.

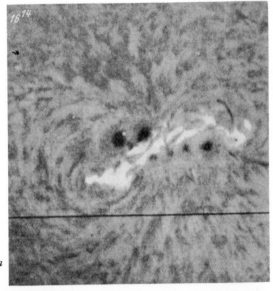

a

b

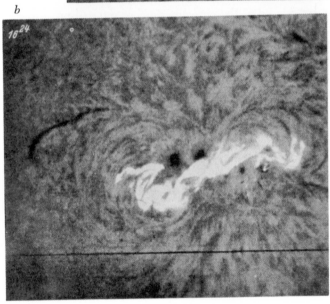

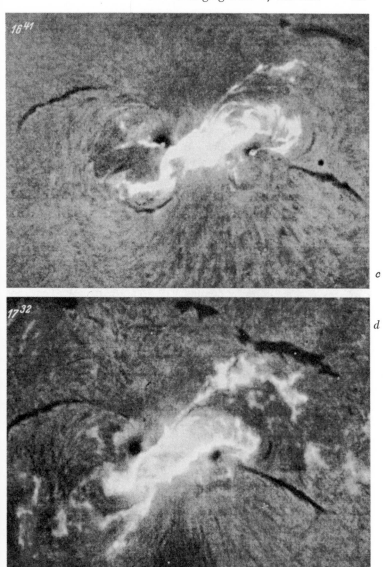

c

d

FIG. 53. Solar flare on April 25, 1946. Photographs were taken at 4:14 p.m., 4:24 p.m., 4:41 p.m. (maximum) and 5:32 p.m. (Meudon).

Flares in the chromosphere

We have seen that sunspots must be the seats of strong electric currents, since all magnetic fields are associated with a flow of electricity. We shall therefore not be surprised to learn that phenomena similar to terrestrial thunderstorms occur on the sun. The lightning flashes are, of course, considerably larger, and, as we might have expected, they are restricted to the vicinity of the spots. Figure 52 shows one such flare bridging the gap between a group of spots. The speed with which flares form and spread is shown clearly by the four consecutive photographs which make up Figure 53. While normal flares must be observed through the spectrohelioscope—in the light of an appropriate spectral line (otherwise they would be lost in the intense glare of the sun)—larger flares can occasionally be observed without special apparatus.

Flares are common phenomena, one large flare and many smaller flares occurring daily near the larger spots. The number of very small flares (that is, flares which may last for only a few minutes) may be well over a hundred per day. The study of flares is not the concern of solar physicists alone, since flares have a direct effect on the earth as well. They emit intense ultraviolet radiation and X rays which affect our ionosphere and with it long-range radio communications (see page 150). Flares also give rise to atomic (corpuscular) radiation, and if any of the emitted particles reach the earth (which happens quite frequently) they disturb the earth's magnetic field with the consequent production of an aurora. Finally, flares emit intense radio waves, and larger flares (classes 3 and 3 +) emit cosmic rays. Cosmic rays are very swift atomic particles with a velocity approaching that of light. The whole of cosmic space seems to be filled with these high-energy particles (see page 109).

Although we know a great deal about the form, the

radiation, and the effects of flares, a complete physical interpretation of this strange phenomenon is still not possible. No doubt, flares, just like terrestrial lightning, must be due to electric discharges resulting from great differences in electric potential. We know that during all such discharges, electrical energy is converted into light and heat, but it would be wrong to apply the results of laboratory experiments to this solar process. Conditions in the solar atmosphere cannot be approximated by any models we may make. Thus, the complicated interplay between solar magnetic fields, the flow of matter and radiation, must be explained theoretically. This is always a hazardous undertaking, but measurements of quick variations in the magnetic field and of the flow of matter in the neighborhood of sunspots ought soon to lead to greater clarity. This work is progressing very favorably.

Flares being of more than purely academic interest, they are nowadays being watched all over the world, and particularly in France, Great Britain, Germany, Italy, Japan, the U.S.S.R., and the U.S.A. Automatic cameras are being used increasingly to take regular films of the sun. The results are compiled daily and published by the U.R.S.I. (Union Radio Scientifique Internationale), in France, Germany, Holland, Japan, and the U.S.A. It appears that flares always occur in association with sunspots and that they, and thus their terrestrial effects, have an 11-year cycle like the spots.

From a physical point of view, flares are of special interest since they contain matter which differs from that in the neighboring regions. Although the flare spectrum is not strikingly different from that of the chromosphere, we have seen that flares emit X rays, radio frequencies, and cosmic rays. During the last 12 years Geiger counters and similar instruments have recorded five sudden increases in the intensity of the solar component of cosmic radiation. Some Russian scientists are

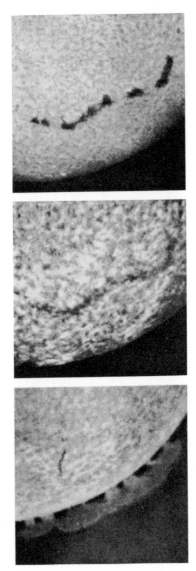

FIG. 54. The migration of a
prominence to the limb due
to the rotation of the sun
(Meudon).

of the opinion that the very luminosity of the chromospheric flares is due to the effect of these rapid, so-called relativistic, particles.

Finally, we must mention that flares can occasionally be observed on other stars also, where they show themselves by sudden increases in the total luminosity. In some cases the luminosity of a star has been known to reach a multiple of its normal value within a matter of minutes.

Prominences: form and lifetime

Prominences might well be called the Alps of the sun. Their height may exceed 100,000 miles, yet these "mountains," impressive though they look through the telescope, are entirely made up of moving gases. They contain very small quantities of matter, the density of a prominence being considerably lower than that of, say, a column of smoke. Their red luminescence against the dark background of the limb is an impressive spectacle, and those of us who have been fortunate enough to watch this sight will understand why so many observers are completely fascinated by it.

Since prominences, like spots and faculae, rotate with the sun, and since they generally have a long lifetime, a comparative study of their structure on consecutive days can be made. Gigantic luminous "trees" or "funnels" at the limb, prominences look like dark snakes when seen against the disk, and are then called filaments. Since limb and disk used to be observed with separate instruments, it took many years before the filaments were identified as prominences. Figure 54 shows one such filament rotating toward the limb, where it suddenly looks brighter than the background. Actually, prominences are always equally bright, but while their luminosity is greater than that of the dark limb, they weaken the light of the photosphere on the disk, just as a candle can cast a shadow on a screen illuminated

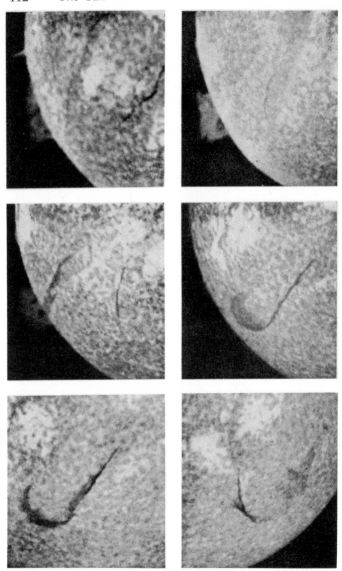

FIG. 55. Prominences are thin bands. The same prominence in six different positions (Meudon).

by a projector. From their filamentous form we know that prominences are narrow bands with the characteristic form seen in Figure 55, which shows the same filament in six different positions. The characteristic dimensions of a normal prominence are roughly: height 18,000 to 60,000 miles, length more than 100,000 miles, width only about 3000 miles.

Birth and metamorphosis of filaments

Like sunspots and faculae, prominences too have a checkered life history. Some of the stages are almost dramatic. Prominences generally arise in the spot belts north and south of the equator, and often close to a group of spots. From the very beginning they have the typical archlike structure shown on Figure 54. A large number of newly formed prominences, most of which never reach full development, is always to be found near a group of spots. In the initial stages, most filaments undergo constant changes. If there are spots in

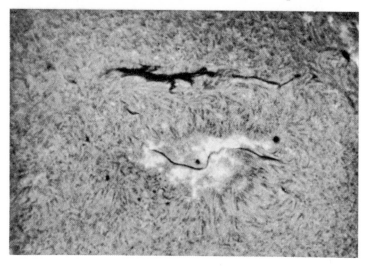

FIG. 56. Newly formed filament inside a group of spots (Fraunhofer Institute, Capri).

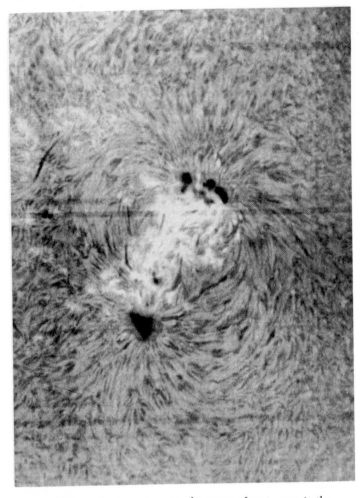

FIG. 57. Chromospheric vortex around a group of spots, seen in the light of hydrogen (Mt. Wilson).

the region, the filament usually points toward the spot with the greatest magnetic field. Occasionally, a filament will disappear, to return one to three days later, its shape almost unchanged. While its length constantly increases, its width and height do not. If a filament

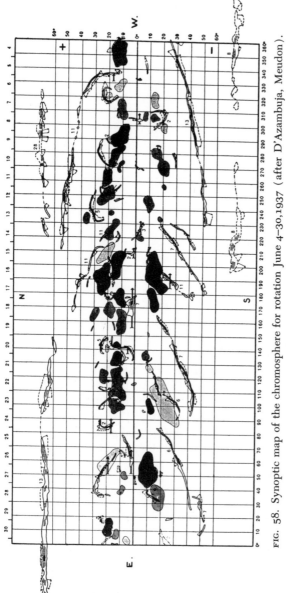

FIG. 58. Synoptic map of the chromosphere for rotation June 4–30, 1937 (after D'Azambuja, Meudon).

manages to survive for a week, it usually reaches a length of about 60,000 miles.

Taken all together, the growing filaments (or prominences) form a continuous structure frequently in the form of a simple vortex or even of two opposing vortices (Fig. 57). These vortices, which can be likened to the movements of terrestrial high and low pressure centers, are caused by the joint effects of the inflow of chromospheric matter and the rotation of the sun. In addition, the magnetic fields in the spots also sensibly affect the form of the vortices which are not, in any case, the causes of the magnetic fields, as was originally thought.

Roughly three weeks after their birth, the filaments assume a stable form and a fixed direction. They now look like long black threads, often more than 500,000 miles long, and fan out like plumes from the equator to the east. This is best shown on synoptic maps of the solar chromosphere (Fig. 58), which give a continuous and detailed chart of filaments, faculae, and spots (arranged by solar rotation). Such maps are compiled independently by different observatories. Dark regions on the map are faculae, the darkness being a measure of their brightness. Circles within each facula represent spots. Comparisons of the shape of filaments during successive rotations of the sun, that is, at intervals of 27 days, show that they tend increasingly to assume directions parallel to the equator. This tendency is the direct consequence of the differential rotation of the sun. An imaginary straight line drawn between the north and south poles of the sun (the so-called central meridian) would be deformed appreciably after only one rotation. Figure 59 shows the forms such a meridian would assume during six consecutive rotations. Filaments, therefore, simply follow the deformation of the solar surface. This was proved conclusively by the intensive investigations of D'Azambuja, a famous French solar physicist.

As the filaments gradually change direction, they

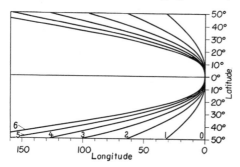

Deformation of the solar meridian after 1, 2 . . . 6 rotations.

keep growing longer and drift toward the poles. In this way they reach ever-higher latitudes, finally to form a polar "crown" of filaments near latitudes 70°N. and S.

The frequency distribution of filaments and prominences in different latitudes varies with the position of the spot belt, and also with the number of spots. Figure 60 shows this distribution for the years 1919–37. The diagram resembles the butterfly diagram in Figure 43, though the latitude distribution of filaments is not as definite as that of the sunspots. This is due to the great length of the filaments.

The development of a prominence

In the course of its development—which lasts many months—almost every prominence goes through an explosive phase. This phase is often preceded by increased internal movements. Some hours later, the prominence will leap out into space with a velocity of up to 450 miles per second. It may leave no trace at all or else only a few dark points. Within a few days a new prominence with the old shape will be formed in the same place. This phenomenon may recur on more than one occasion. Figure 61 illustrates the different stages of an explosion which, in this case, caused the prominence to rise with a velocity of about 125 miles per second.

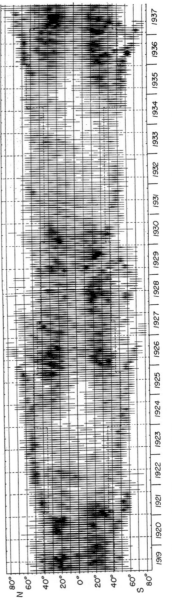

FIG. 60. "Butterfly" diagram of filaments 1919–37.

A prominence may also make an explosive *disappearance* into the chromosphere (Fig. 62). The figure shows a surge from the chromosphere (the bright arc round the metal cone of the coronagraph) shooting up with a velocity of about 450 miles per second. While the surge does not appear to touch the prominence, it has a disturbing effect on it, and, quite suddenly, the prominence matter begins to stream into well-defined trajectories which curve to the right and downward into the chromosphere, and often toward a sunspot. These trajectories seem to be fixed in space. Time after time the luminous prominence matter can be seen to follow the same curved paths. It is thought that these trajectories coincide with the magnetic lines of force of the neighboring sunspots. This explains why the prominence matter, instead of dropping vertically toward the sun's center of gravity, follows a curved path, as would a compass needle. It is also believed that prominences are normally kept hovering above the surface of the sun by the action of a magnetic field. When this magnetic field changes, strong electric currents are induced inside the prominence. These currents are repulsed by the magnetic field and, as a reaction, the prominence and the surrounding corona are thrown out into space. Prominences are therefore extremely sensitive indicators of the form of, and the changes in, magnetic fields, many of which are too weak to be measured spectroscopically.

The regular reappearance of prominences in the same place and with the same form may perhaps be attributed to the presence of magnetic fields also. A closer study of magnetic fields will certainly go a long way toward solving this question (see page 129).

What is a prominence?

We have now examined the birth, the motion, and the explosion of prominences and the forces involved.

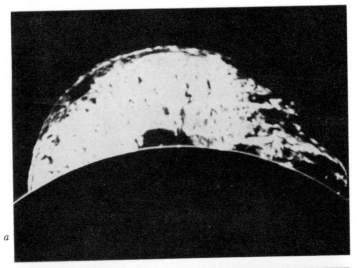

a

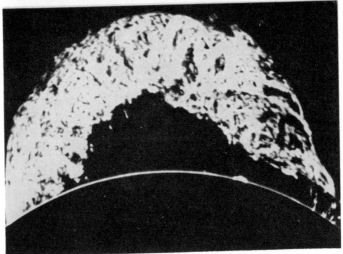

b

FIG. 61. An explosion on the sun. Rising prominence in four stages. Photographs taken at 4:03 p.m., 4:36 p.m., 4:51 p.m., 5:03 p.m. on June 4, 1946 (W. O. Roberts, Climax).

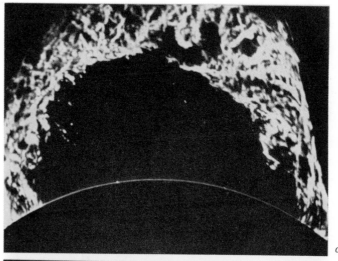

c

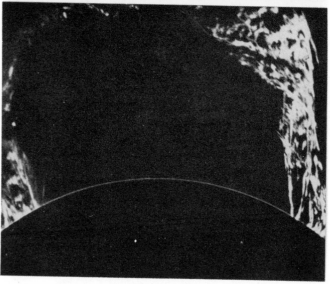

d

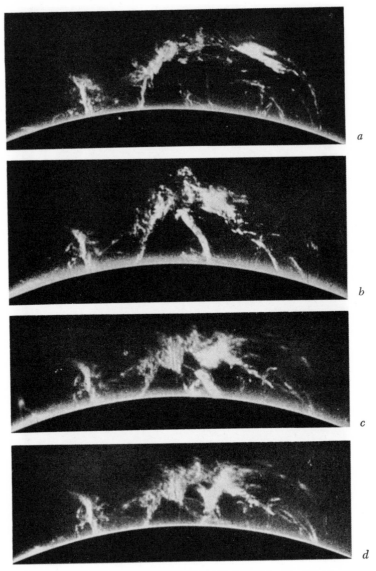

FIG. 62. A chromospheric surge causes a prominence to flow downwards. Photographs taken at 12:45 p.m., 12:49 p.m., 12:54 p.m., 1:25 p.m. on June 12, 1937 (Lyot, Pic du Midi).

But what of the prominences themselves? Are they solar clouds? Prominences have a density roughly 100 times that of the coronal gases, and as prominences seem to form spontaneously in the (generally invisible) corona, it seems probable that their matter is derived from it, just as terrestrial clouds are formed by the condensations of invisible water vapor. The observed fact that gas in the corona is rarefied in the vicinity of prominences supports this assumption, since the "condensation" of a prominence would absorb a considerable volume of coronal gases (in the ratio of 1 : 100). Another observation points in the same direction: as the rapid currents within a prominence seem to flow mainly in a downward direction, the prominences ought to disappear into the chromosphere after only a few days. However, as they last for months, they must constantly be drawing on matter from the corona. Thus, the actual condensation mechanism apart, the analogy with our own clouds is almost complete. Prominences are a kind of "rain" in which condensed coronal matter is constantly poured down into the chromosphere.

Finally, a few words about the peculiar way in which prominences keep growing longer and longer. A simple experiment will help to explain this strange phenomenon. If we place a glass of water on a slowly rotating phonograph turntable and introduce a drop of ink halfway along the radius of the glass, the drop will sink and be stretched into a narrow band of ink. Seen from the top, this band will look like a thin spiraling thread. In the experiment, the appearance of the thread is due to the fact that the water rotates more quickly at the edge of the glass than at the center. This differential rotation is the joint result of gravity and the Coriolis force. (The Coriolis force is associated with the rotation of all bodies.) In the experiment the drop of ink represents the prominence, and the rotating glass of water represents the differential rotation of the solar corona in which the prominence is situated. Gravity has the same effect in both cases. Our simple experiment has therefore shown us how the threadlike structure of the prominence must be the result of the interaction between the corona, the force of gravity, and the rotation of the sun.

Solar storms

We have now discussed all the phenomena which occur in the vicinity of sunspots. None of these phenomena is the primary cause of any of the others, the original cause lying deep within the sun. The totality of all visible phenomena accompanying the formation of a sunspot group is called a center of activity. Figure 63 shows the life history of a typical center of activity in simplified drawings. The birth of the center is heralded by a facular speck. On the second day this speck has increased considerably and bears a small spot. By the fifth day the facula has grown rapidly both in size and brightness, and an increasing number of spots now form a bipolar group. On about the eleventh day the spots have reached their maximum development. Small filaments may appear. By the twenty-seventh day the spots are much smaller, and only one very long filament has survived. The facula has nearly reached its maximum brightness. On the fifty-fourth day, that is, after two rotations of the sun the spots have completely disappeared and the facula is cut in half by the now even longer filament. The filament turns increasingly toward east-west—parallel to the equator. After four rotations of the sun (108 days) the facula has disappeared, and only the filament remains with a maximum length of about 200,000 miles. After a further four to six rotations, the filament, too, begins to dissolve, and the solar surface is ready to return to its normal smooth appearance. The activity center disappears without leaving a trace.

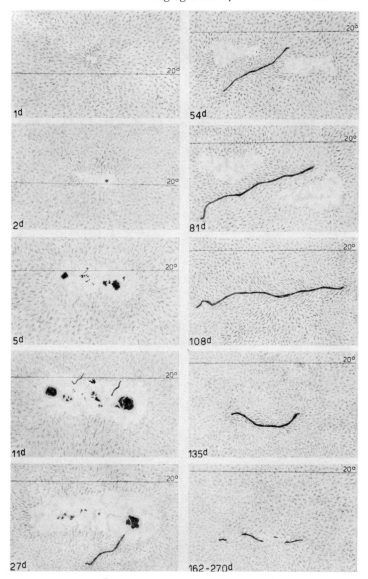

FIG. 63. The development of an activity center.

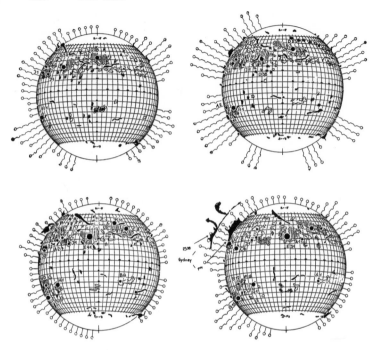

FIG. 64. Daily maps of the sun, April 8–15, 1956. Prominences and facular regions in their natural form. The figures give the number of spots in a particular group. Thus, D38 means that the group is of type D and consists of 38 spots. The marginal rays measure the intensity of the green coronal line on the limb (Fraunhofer Institute, Freiburg).

The life history of an activity center is also reflected in the corona. Since the corona can be observed only on the limb the results are less complete. During the lifetime of a facula, the corona above it looks brighter both in white light and also in the light of some coronal lines (see page 75). This increase in brightness indicates an intensified scattering of sunlight, that is, a concentration of electrons. Thus, the corona is denser over a center of activity than it is over normal regions. The intensification of line radiation—particularly of the

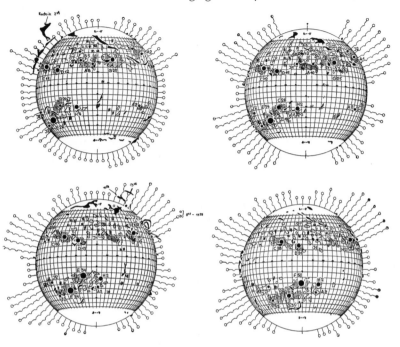

green coronal line 5303 A. and the red line 6374 A.—
indicates an associated rise in gas temperature. Above
an activity center the normally high temperature of the
corona is raised by an additional amount of a few hundred thousand degrees (compare the rise of temperature
in chromospheric faculae).

Observing the sun

Just as meteorologists carefully watch and record
meteorological data, so solar physicists keep constant
watch over the solar surface. But while the meteor-
ologist has to compile his charts from observations taken
at thousands of weather stations, the solar explorer can
survey an entire hemisphere at once.

Even so, his constant vigil is impeded by clouds and by the fall of night, and so the continuous observation of the sun also calls for a world-wide net of astronomers. This network has been established during the last 20 years and has increased its efforts particularly since the last war.

The reasons for this co-operation are not purely astronomical. During World War II it became perfectly obvious how much solar activity affects our ionosphere and hence long-distance radio communications (see page 150). The study of solar activity is therefore also the study of the conditions for good reception.

Nowadays, sunspots are being counted by innumerable astronomers and amateurs, so that a continuous picture can easily be obtained. On the other hand, the continuous survey of the chromosphere and the corona is still impeded by snags. These are due less to climatic or nocturnal interruptions than to the difficulty of obtaining compatible quantitative results from the different observatories.

Diary of the sun

The synoptic maps of the photosphere (issued by the Zurich observatory) and of the chromosphere (issued by the Paris-Meudon Observatory—see Fig. 58) give only an average picture for one particular rotation of the sun. However, daily maps have been published since 1956. Compiled by a host of collaborators in a large number of observatories round the globe, these daily maps give an almost continuous diary of the sun for 24 hours of the day. Figure 64 shows eight such maps published by the Fraunhofer Institute in Freiburg, Germany, in collaboration with the following observatories: Arcetri-Florence, Athens, Boulder (U.S.A.), Florence, Capri, Greenwich, Istanbul, Kanzelhöhe (Austria), Kodaikanal (India), Meudon-Paris, Potsdam, Prague, Sacramento Peak (U.S.A.), Sydney, Tokyo,

Tonantzintla (Mexico), Uccle (Belgium), Wendelstein (Germany).

The Lyot filter

The reliability of chromosphere surveys in particular has increased considerably since the birefringent interference filter, first proposed by Lyot and independently by Öhman, has begun to take the place of the complicated and clumsy spectroheliographs. Such filters pass a single spectral line only, and the ingenious use of biaxial quartz and spar crystals in them makes it possible to take photographs of the chromosphere with exposures of 1/50 second (the spectroheliograph must be exposed for a few minutes). At least 20 such instruments have been installed in different observatories, and with them the "hunt," particularly for flares (of which more than 90 per cent are being "caught") is now in full cry. Figures 52 and 56 were taken with this type of filter.

Magnetograms of the sun

A watch is also being kept over the magnetic fields of the sun. While strong fields near sunspots have been recorded since 1908 at Mount Wilson Observatory—and to a lesser extent at the Einstein Tower in Potsdam—more recently it became possible to make a regular record of even the very weak magnetic fields in other regions. The very complicated instrument used for this purpose—once again at Mount Wilson Observatory—incorporates a photoelectric detector which measures the very small deflections in certain lines of the solar spectrum (caused by the presence of weak magnetic fields) with a degree of accuracy far exceeding that of classical photographical or visual methods. Figure 65 shows two such magnetic records (magnetograms) taken on consecutive days.

Many such instruments—called magnetographs—are

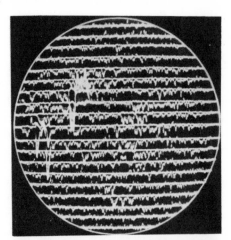

a

b

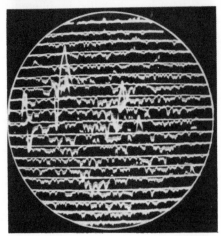

FIG. 65. Magnetograms of the sun. Deflections of the curve give the intensity of the magnetic field (Babcock, Mt. Wilson).

in the process of being built and soon we shall have a complete picture of the changes occurring in the magnetic fields of the sun. As we have seen, magnetic fields affect the course of almost all observable solar phenomena. Once they are fully understood, therefore, we shall have a far better understanding of all the complex phenomena associated with the solar activity.

Observations of the corona

The constant survey of the corona (which can only be observed directly in a narrow slice round the limb) is even more difficult to obtain than a continuous magnetic record. Although the versatile Lyot has perfected a photoelectric procedure which gives good results even when the sky is not perfectly blue and even at lower altitudes, most observers still use the antiquated and clumsy visual and photographic methods which are appreciably affected by the terrestrial atmosphere. Only when Lyot's method is universally accepted can we hope to have anything approaching a continuous and quantitative record.

On the other hand, the observation of solar radio emission has reached a high degree of perfection, and this despite the relative novelty of radio astronomy. Not only can radio frequencies be received even when the sky is overcast, but most radio astronomers, being familiar with high-frequency techniques, are experts in building instruments for making continuous, automatic records.

The international efforts to record the optical, magnetic, and emissive properties of the sun will doubtless lead to better knowledge of the solar atmosphere than any astronomer would have dared to hope not so very long ago.

VIII. *The Interior of the Sun*

Optical instruments can do no more than probe a very thin surface layer of the sun. To explain processes inside the sun we must construct a theoretical model. This model must explain the observed surface temperature, the observed radiation, and the total mass of the sun, in accordance with all the rules of physics. We know, for instance, that at every point in the sun the force of gravity (tending to contract the sun) and the gas pressure (tending to expand the sun) must be in equilibrium, otherwise the sun could not have retained its size and brightness for millions of years. From these conditions of mechanical equilibrium alone, it follows that the central solar temperature must be about 27,000,-000°F. Only at that temperature is the gas pressure great enough to balance the enormous force of gravity. The pressure is, in fact, so great that matter at the center of the sun must be compressed to a density of about 100 grams per cubic centimeter. A matchbox filled with solar matter would here weigh more than two pounds.

The sun is a gigantic atomic reactor

The sun radiates a kilowatt of energy on every square meter of the earth's surface. The same quantity of energy falls on every square meter of the surface of the gigantic shell of which the earth's orbit about the sun is the circumference—a sphere whose radius is roughly 93,-000,000 miles. This radiation must have been emitted by the sun for at least a billion years, because the oldest discovered organic fossils have an estimated life of about that order. Had the sun's radiation been only a fraction weaker at the time, the earth's temperature would have been such that no organic processes could ever have developed.

How does the sun obtain this gigantic supply of energy? More than a hundred years ago, Helmholtz and Kelvin calculated that if the sun were heated by its own contraction, the supply of energy would be exhausted after only 24,000,000 years. (Were the sun made up of best quality coal, it would have burnt out within 8,000 years.) Eddington in 1925, and Bethe and Weizsäcker in 1938 then drew the (now) fairly obvious conclusion that subatomic (or as we say nuclear) energy was being released in the deep interior of the sun. No other explanation could account for the fantastic energies liberated by the sun or, for that matter, by any other star. The existence of this type of energy was first suspected when high-velocity particles were observed to emanate from decaying radioactive atoms (natural radioactivity). At that time it was already known that the energy contained in the atomic nucleus was roughly a million times greater than that liberated during the chemical combination of individual atoms.

Energy has weight

How can atoms be made to relinquish this latent nuclear energy? The reader may know that the atomic nucleus of a given chemical element consists of protons (hydrogen nuclei) and neutrons, in such a way that an atom with atomic number Z and atomic weight A has Z protons and A–Z neutrons. Now, the total mass of a heavy atomic nucleus was found to be less than the mass of its constituent protons and neutrons. This difference between the observed mass (measured with a mass spectrometer) and the theoretical mass of the individual particles is called the mass defect. Thus, when a hydrogen nucleus was built out of protons and neutrons, the new nucleus showed a defect of 0.03028 the mass of the hydrogen atom. Again, when protons and neutrons weighing 1 gram were combined into helium, 0.00757 grams, about 0.75 per cent of the total mass, was found to have disappeared. Something had apparently gone wrong with the whole of classical physics, based as it is on the laws of the conservation of mass and of energy.

This difficulty was solved more than 50 years ago when Albert Einstein in his general theory of relativity proposed the equivalence of mass and energy. This equivalence is expressed by the equation $E = mc^2$, where E is the energy, m the mass, and c the velocity of light (186,000 miles a second). It follows from the equation that a gram of mass is equivalent to 9.10^{20} ergs or 25,000,000 kilowatt hours. If matter could therefore be changed into energy, a few grams of matter would be able to supply the daily energy needed on earth. From the same equation it also follows that hot bodies must be heavier than cold bodies since heat is a form of energy and as such must have weight, though, from Einstein's equation, it can be shown that normally this weight is infinitesimally small.

Let us now return to the sun. According to Einstein's equation, the formation of helium from protons and neutrons must liberate a quantity of energy equal to the mass defect multiplied by c^2. This was shown to be the case, even though the detection of this energy was not nearly as simple as the detection of the energy liberated by normal chemical reactions. Thus, nuclear physics has proved the validity of Einstein's equation— the construction or annihilation of atomic nuclei liberates or absorbs a quantity of energy corresponding to the change in mass.

Nuclear reactions in the sun

If energy is to be derived from atomic nuclei, these nuclei must first be built up. In atomic reactors this is done by bombarding a heavy element, for instance

uranium, with neutrons. The uncharged neutron pene-
trates the uranium nucleus and causes it to break up.
In this process two further neutrons are ejected which,
in turn, can explode other uranium nuclei, etc. The
whole reactor would blow up like an atom bomb if
there were no way of curbing this chain reaction. Hence
the neutrons are slowed down in a so-called moderator.
The resulting (controlled) heat is used to produce steam
in an external jacket, and the steam is then made to
drive a turbine.

In principle, processes in a star are similar to those
in the atomic reactor, although different chemical elements and different bombarding particles are involved.
Inside the sun, as we have seen, the planetary electrons are swept away from the atoms, the remaining
nuclei colliding with tremendous velocity. In this way
heavy nuclei are built up from the lighter nuclei. The
energy liberated in this reaction (high energy particles
or short-wave lengths) is converted into heat as it hits
the gaseous outer layers which are comparable to the
steam jacket of our reactor. From this gaseous "wall"
heat and light rays are then emitted into space. All the
energy must be provided by a corresponding mass defect in the reacting nuclei. Now, the relativistic mass
of the radiation leaving the sun per second is 3,600,000
tons, which happens to be the exact mass defect per
second in the solar interior.

Possible nuclear processes

Since the center of the sun is made up of more than
one element, a number of different nuclear reactions are
possible. A hydrogen nucleus may collide with a carbon
nucleus to convert it into a nitrogen nucleus, or two
normal hydrogen nuclei (protons) may collide to form
a heavy hydrogen nucleus. Most, but not all, possible
nuclear processes inside the sun are known largely from
laboratory experiments, that is, from investigations of
natural and artificial atomic reactions. In the laboratory,

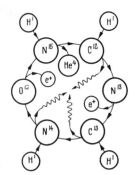

FIG. 66. The carbon-nitrogen cycle.

however, the atomic projectiles are not accelerated by heat but by gigantic electric accelerators (betatrons, synchrotrons, and cosmotrons).

Some solar reactions can only be explained by theoretical considerations of the probable behavior of two different nuclei. Of the many possible reactions between the nuclei of the most common chemical elements in the sun (hydrogen, helium, carbon, nitrogen, oxygen, neon, magnesium, silicon, and iron), two reactions are particularly important: the carbon-nitrogen cycle and the proton-proton cycle. In both cycles, helium is built up from hydrogen nuclei, with a consequent transformation of mass into energy. However, helium is built up differently in each cycle.

Figure 66 is a diagrammatic sketch of the carbon-nitrogen cycle. Starting, for instance, with ordinary carbon (C^{12}), we see that if it collides with a hydrogen nucleus H^1 (a proton), a lighter isotope of nitrogen (N^{13}) is formed. N^{13} being unstable, it is spontaneously transformed into the stable nucleus of the heavier carbon isotope (C^{13}) within ten minutes, emitting a positive electron in the process. If C^{13} is hit by a further hydrogen nucleus, it is converted into ordinary nitrogen (N^{14}). If the nucleus of N^{14} collides with a further hydrogen nucleus, N^{14} is converted into an unstable oxygen isotope (O^{15}) which, similar to N^{13}, changes spontaneously into the stable N^{15} through the emission of a positive electron. If, finally, N^{15} collides with yet another hydrogen nucleus, it is converted into a C^{12} (with which we began) together with a helium nucleus or a-particle. At the end of this cycle four hydrogen nuclei have thus become converted into a helium nucleus. The original carbon and nitrogen nuclei are forever being regenerated in this cycle and act as catalysts, as chemists would call them. In this process energy is liberated in the form of two high-velocity positive electrons and two high-frequency γ-rays. The individual processes of the cycle are not of equal duration and depend on temperature and density. In the sun, which has an internal temperature of about 27,-000,000°F. and a density of about 100 grams per cubic centimeter, the complete cycle is of the order of 10,-000,000 years. The liberation of so much energy over so long a period must be attributed to the immense number of atomic nuclei participating in the process.

Another, and parallel, cycle in the sun is the proton-proton cycle, in which helium is built up from hydrogen directly, without a catalyst, in the following way:

Hydrogen nucleus H^1 + hydrogen nucleus H^1
$\rightarrow$ heavy hydrogen nucleus H^2 + positron + γ-radiation

Heavy hydrogen nucleus H^2 + hydrogen nucleus H^1
$\rightarrow$ helium nucleus He^3 + γ-radiation

Helium nucleus He^3 + helium nucleus He^3
$\rightarrow$ helium nucleus He^4 + 2 hydrogen nuclei H^1.

In the interior of the sun, the quantity of energy liberated in this process would seem to be comparable with that liberated in the carbon cycle. While the proton cycle is probably the chief source of energy in stars cooler than the sun, the carbon-nitrogen cycle would seem to be the main source in hotter stars.

IX. Radio Waves from the Sun

As long ago as 1893, a few years after Heinrich Hertz's discovery of radio waves, it seemed probable that the solar corona, believed to be a gigantic electric discharge itself, could emit this type of radiation also. Some years later still, French and British investigators made unsuccessful attempts to "receive" the sun. The receivers were inadequate, and even when solar radio waves were finally picked up with better sets in 1937, they were not recognized as such. Their real discovery was not made until 1942, when British radar operators managed to detect them. Despite wartime preoccupations, this news spread like wildfire, and as soon as the war was over a new scientific discipline—radio astronomy—began to make giant strides. Within two decades radio observatories have been established all over the world, and almost as much money is being spent on radio as on other astronomical research. Nowadays, a large proportion of astronomical and astrophysical literature consists of radio-astronomical publications.

Radio waves and light waves

Before we take a closer look at cosmic radio waves, we must contrast them with light waves. Hertz established quite clearly that light and radio waves are of the same nature, though they have different origins and wave lengths. Figure 67 tabulates the wave lengths and frequencies (number of oscillations per second) of all known radiation. All X rays, and some ultraviolet

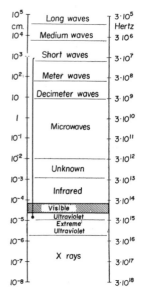

FIG. 67. Scale of wave lengths.

radiation (including all extreme ultraviolet rays) have been absorbed by atmospheric oxygen and nitrogen by the time they are within 60 miles of the earth. This radiation can, therefore, not penetrate to even the highest mountain peaks.

Radio waves apart, the only wave lengths which can reach the earth through the "window" of the atmosphere coincide with the visible spectrum (wave lengths between 4000 A. and 7000 A., or between 4/100,000 and 7/100,000 cm). This range contains all the known colors. The water vapor of our atmosphere acts as a screen excluding all wave lengths from the extreme red up to waves of about 1 cm, that is the shortest radio waves. Radio waves can penetrate another "window" in the atmosphere at wave lengths between 1 cm and 15 m. The even longer cosmic waves are kept out by the ionosphere, which also bends back terrestrial radio waves. If these rectilinear waves were not so bent back they would escape into space and could not be received all over the world (see page 152).

An ideal radiator—technically known as a black body —will, depending only on its temperature, emit any of the wave lengths shown in Figure 67, though with different intensities. It is now known that the sun behaves very much like such an ideal radiator, though the detection of some of its radiation is difficult and involves the use of special instruments. While visible light can be detected by eye, by telescope, etc., the sun's ultraviolet rays can only be measured from rockets at heights of more than 60 miles. The detection of infrared radiation presents special difficulties and what little of it passes through the water vapor in the atmosphere can only be measured by special photoelectric cells. Finally, radio waves can only be received by special aerials in conjunction with electronic equipment.

Radio telescopes

The instrument for detecting cosmic radiation is the radio telescope, though the term "telescope" is a little misleading. While an ordinary telescope produces an image, a radio telescope simply measures the total intensity of the received radiation in roughly the same way that an exposure meter, instead of giving complete pictures, only measures average light intensities. To give a complete "picture" of the sources of the radio waves, the radio telescope must scan each point. It is as if we used an exposure meter to give the light intensity of each part of an object and then made a complete picture by fitting together the individual parts as in a mosaic.

This is done in the case of the radio telescope by directing the aerial at different point sources. Thus, in "looking" at the sun, its aperture angle must be considerably smaller than the apparent solar diameter. This is an extremely difficult task and constitutes the chief

FIG. 68. Radio telescope for receiving wave length 11 cm (Fraunhofer Institute).

technical problem of radio astronomy.

The resolving power of a radio telescope is its power of distinguishing two separate points. The telescope can only distinguish two points whose angular separation is less than 1.22 λ/D, where λ is the wave length and D the diameter of the telescope objective (Rayleigh's criterion). The greater the wave length of the source, therefore, the greater must be the diameter of the objective. Thus, a good objective of diameter 10 cm can still distinguish a coin 6 miles away in green light (wave length 5/100,000 cm).

Now, the wave lengths received by a radio telescope happen to be many million times longer than those of normal light, and so the diameter of the receiver must be correspondingly large. In the case of our coin, the diameter of the mirror aerial would have to be 60 miles.

Thus, even the largest radio telescope—the one at Jo-drell Bank, which has a reflecting surface 250 feet in diameter—has a far smaller resolving power than the simplest optical telescope.

The radio telescope is constructed on simple lines. A movable parabolic metal reflector (Fig. 68) concentrates the incident radio waves upon a receiving aerial, placed at the focus. The incoming signal is amplified so that its strength can be read from a dial. The dial is graduated by first being connected to a transmitter of known strength.

Instead of the reflector, an array of aerials consisting of suitably spaced dipoles can be used (Fig. 69). Such systems of aerials are particularly suited to receiving wave lengths longer than 50 cm. Reflectors and aerials alike are generally mounted equatorially—on a rotating axis parallel to the earth's polar axis. In this way they can be made to "follow" a star across the sky.

FIG. 69. Equatorially mounted system of directional aerials (Yagi).

FIG. 70. Radio-interferometer for receiving wave length 21 cm (Sydney).

Interferometers

We have seen that radio telescopes have a weak resolving power, too weak, in fact, to scan the sun's disk or even the Milky Way. We have also seen that at a given radio wave length the resolving power is determined by the diameter of the reflector or the aerials. Though the diameter of a reflector cannot reasonably be increased to more than about 100 meters, a consideration of the way in which the incoming waves are bent back at the edge of the mirror (or the aerial) shows that maximum resolving power is obtained by using an array of smaller reflectors representing the edge of an (imaginary) large reflector. The individual reflectors are joined to a single receiver. Such systems —which, as it were, help to outwit the waves—are known as interferometers. Some existing interferometers represent reflectors with diameters of a few kilometers. Figure 70 shows an interferometer consisting of 30 individual reflectors.

As the radio astronomer points his giant reflectors at the sky, all he hears is a soft rushing sound which is occasionally intensified into a clicking noise.

If he happens to be watching the sun during times when there are no sunspots, he will receive nearly uniform radio waves, the intensity of the signal depending on the wave length to which the receiver is tuned. This "undisturbed" solar radiation can now be received in a range of wave lengths between 1 cm (30,000 Mc/s) and 15 m (20 Mc/s). The radiation has the same cause as the solar spectrum (or the light emitted by any body at a high temperature). Its intensity varies with the temperature of the radiator.

The radio sun is larger than the optical sun

There is one difference between solar radio waves and solar light waves: while all the light waves come from one layer—the photosphere—different radio waves come from different strata of the solar atmosphere. Centimeter waves (3 to about 15 cm)—like light waves—reveal only the photosphere, and their intensity was, in fact, found to correspond to the temperature of the photospheric atmosphere (about 6000°). Wave lengths longer than 50 cm are considerably weakened by the ionized gases of the solar atmosphere. Thus, only those from the corona can escape freely into space, and, in fact, the intensity of these waves was found to correspond to the very high temperature of the coronal gases—to about 1,800,000°F. The solar corona which, because of its weak light, is difficult to observe optically (and then only at the limb), can therefore be detected over the entire disk through the intense radio waves it emits. Because the corona reaches far into space, the radio sun appears to be much larger than the light sun.

Since radio waves can penetrate clouds, radio telescopes have a great advantage over optical instruments which cannot be used in bad weather. However, a great

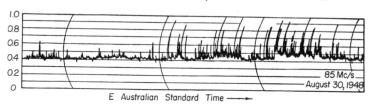

FIG. 71. Enhanced solar radiation. Record taken between 12:15 a.m. and 2:00 p.m.

deal of technical work still remains to be done before a complete radio picture of the solar surface and the solar corona can be obtained.

Solar radio bursts

Side by side with normal radio waves, the sun also emits sporadic waves which may be many million times as intense. This sporadic radiation is closely related to the solar activity—to sunspots, faculae, flares, and changes in the corona. Such fluctuations in intensity, the so-called bursts or outbursts, may last for a few days, for a few hours, for minutes or only for seconds. The bursts can appear individually or in groups. Figure 71 is a record of the intensity of the wave length 3.50 m (85 Mc/s), one of the wave lengths emitted by the corona. The record shows a great many sudden increases in intensity, each lasting for only a few seconds.

Short waves of about 10 cm (300 Mc/s) have daily, far less violent, fluctuations in intensity. A continuous record of these fluctuations shows a marked parallelism with the number of sunspots (Fig. 72). In fact, the correlation between this 10 cm wave and the sunspot number is so good that even with an overcast sky we can now make relatively reliable deductions about the number of sunspots.

Far more intensive radiation is emitted during outbursts. Frequently, but not always, they are associated

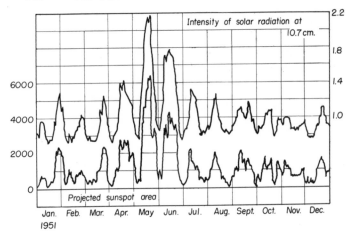

FIG. 72. Intensity of solar radiation at wave length 10.7 cm (top) and projected area of sunspots (bottom).

with the appearance of chromospheric flares. The intensity of an outburst may become so great that it can be picked up with an ordinary V.H.F. receiver. Oddly enough, outbursts on different wave lengths reach the earth at different times.

While the outburst is first received on the wave length 1.50 m (200 Mc/s), it is received on wave length 3 m (100 Mc/s) two minutes later, and as much as six minutes later on wave length 5 m (60 Mc/s). If we remember that each wave comes from a different level of the sun, it follows that the source of the outburst must be moving out from the surface of the sun with a velocity of about 300 miles per second. Many such movements through the solar corona have been "followed" with large radio interferometers during the past few years, and these observations have confirmed, more or less, the deductions made from the time lag in the arrival of the different radio waves.

While the interpretation of normal solar radio waves presents no difficulty (they are the natural result of the sun's temperature, and would be emitted by any other body at that temperature), outbursts are still causing radio astronomers many headaches. Their intensity is so large that they cannot possibly be explained by the thermal properties of solar matter. Unlike the weaker, normal radiation of the sun which corresponds to a random motion of electrons in the solar atmosphere, outbursts must be due to an ordered motion of electrons superposed on their random thermal motions. Conditions inside the solar transmitter can therefore be compared to conditions in ordinary radio transmitters in which electrons are forced to oscillate in definite trajectories (coils, valves, etc.). While the details of the mechanism in the sun are not yet fully understood, it would seem that collisions between streams of fast-moving particles (or pressure waves) and the interactions between the electrons and positive ions in these streams must play a decisive part. Radio waves can be produced artificially by shooting a stream of electrons through a gas, and, similarly, we have evidence that whenever matter is in rapid motion on the sun or in space, intense radio waves are emitted.

Occasionally these rapid streams of solar matter manage to hit the earth and disturb its magnetic field appreciably. Such corpuscular streams consist of protons and electrons, and the more intense ones are probably emitted in the neighborhood of sunspots. It is known that this corpuscular radiation is only emitted (and can only disturb the magnetic field of the earth) when the responsible sunspot happens to be a source of intense radio emission also. Thus, corpuscular radiation is always associated with solar radio waves, and the continuous record of these radio waves is therefore a measure of corpuscular radiation and the consequent disturbance of the earth's magnetic field. Since radio waves arrive on earth one day earlier than the corpuscular storms, such disturbances can be predicted.

The scope of this book is such that we cannot give a complete account of all the findings made by radio astronomy in the last five years. Radio astronomy is continuing to make swift progress and has given a glowing example of the value of co-operation between various branches of science: physics, astrophysics, and radio technology.

x. *The Sun and the Earth*

All our plants, all our meteorological processes, and all our supplies of energy—wind, water power, wood, coal, oil, and gas—are ultimately derived from the sun's rays. Our planet would be devoid of all life and vegetation were it not for the fact that the sun has shone down on the earth for at least a billion years.

Balance of energy

Vertical sunlight produces one kilowatt of energy per square meter of the earth's surface or, in other units, two calories per square centimeter per minute. Since the aggregate temperature of the earth as a whole does not change, the earth must re-emit whatever quantity of heat it receives from the sun, no matter whether that heat has gone into evaporating water or whether its uneven effects on land and ocean have given rise to wind or ocean currents. In the end, all these processes always release heat. Just as solar heat reaches the earth in the form of radiation, so the earth must release its thermal energy in the form of radiation also—only electromagnetic rays can travel through empty interplanetary space. Even so, radiation from the sun differs characteristically from terrestrial radiation—not in intensity but in quality. While white sunlight is most intense in the green part of the spectrum, the earth, corresponding to its lower temperature, emits mainly invisible infrared radiation. Despite the fact that it represents the same quantity of energy, infrared radiation cannot be harnessed to do useful work, and does not, for instance, change weather conditions. The physicist would say that the entropy of the energy system has increased or that its thermodynamic efficiency has decreased.

Since the earth's axis is not vertical to the plane of the ecliptic (the earth's orbit about the sun), the obliquity of the sun's rays produces seasonal changes, each hemisphere receiving different quantities of solar radiation at different times of the year. The differences in the radiation received by the two hemispheres, together with the differential heating of ocean and land masses and the resulting large-scale ocean and air currents, make up our weather. If the weather changes from year to year, despite the regularity of the seasons, this must be due to the fact that weather conditions are more or less chaotic, despite the regular supply of solar energy that goes into them. If the sun were to shine evenly over the entire surface of the earth, we should still have large-scale droughts and floods.

The weather and sunspots

Even so, there is no doubt that certain large-scale weather processes are associated with solar phenomena, though it is still unclear whether these processes are set off by fluctuations of the solar constant—which has not yet been measured accurately enough—or by some kind of invisible solar radiation. Once this question is decided, we should be able to forecast large-scale weather changes far more accurately than we can at present.

Radio communication and sunspots

The connection between solar phenomena and the quality of radio reception is even closer. Since radio waves are transmitted in straight lines, we should never be able to receive signals from below the horizon were it not for the fact that the ionosphere (60 to 200 miles above the earth) acts as a giant reflector of radio waves.

The ionosphere has roughly the same chemical constitution as the rest of the terrestrial atmosphere, but, since it is much more exposed to the sun's intensive ultraviolet and X rays, many of its nitrogen and oxygen atoms become ionized with the result that electrons are liberated. Ionized gases have much the same electrical properties as metals. The stronger the source of the ionization (short wave lengths from the sun) the more electrons are stripped from the atoms, and the better the conductivity of the gases. Their reflective properties also depend on the density of the liberated electrons, that is, on the intensity of the ionizing solar radiation. Theoretical considerations have shown that the most intense radio frequency—the shortest wave length—reflected by the ionosphere, the so-called critical frequency, depends very closely on the electron density of the ionosphere. A continuous record of critical frequencies is being kept all over the world, and long-term observations have shown a remarkable correlation between critical frequency and sunspots.

This result is of the greatest practical and astronomical importance. In practical terms it means that radio transmitters can use higher frequencies during sunspot maxima than they can during sunspot minima. In astronomical terms it means that sunspots are associated with emission of ultraviolet and X rays. Though we can-

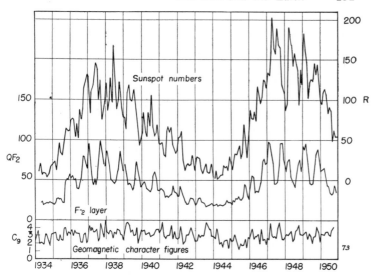

FIG. 73. Critical frequencies and sunspot numbers.

not see or photograph this radiation which is completely absorbed at heights of more than 60 miles, it is quite certain that most of it must come from the hot chromospheric and coronal clouds, from the neighborhood of groups of spots, from faculae, and from the hot coronal regions above the sunspots. Thus, apart from high-altitude rockets, the ionosphere is our only means of measuring processes which can never be observed from the ground.

Fading in radio communication

Long-distance radio communication may occasionally break down completely for no mechanical reason. The fading may last up to an hour and is the direct result of the appearance of a chromospheric flare. Flares, apart from their normal emission of light are a source of intense X rays which, because of their extremely short wave lengths can cross through the E and F layers of the ionosphere. Only at heights less than 60 miles from the ground (where there is a far greater abundance of neutral atoms than in the higher layers) are the X rays stopped by collision with, and ionization of, neutral atoms. While the electrons in the higher layers can move about freely to form a barrier reflecting the radio waves, the electrons freed by the ionization of the lower layers collide with the much more abundant neutral atoms to which they impart their own kinetic energy. Thus, the electrons heat the atoms instead of re-emitting their energy in the form of radio waves. In this layer radio waves are not reflected but damped. Hence this layer is known as the D layer.

Within a few minutes of the appearance of a flare, the D layer, which is present all the time though only with weak intensity, becomes so dense that radio communications on the day side of the earth break down completely (all waves reflected by the ionosphere must cross the D layer at least twice).

Other, less radical, interruptions of radio communications may last for some days, and are generally due to the fact that the ionosphere becomes deformed by geomagnetic storms (see page 153) which change its reflective properties.

The sun disturbs the earth's magnetic field

The earth has a much weaker magnetic field than the sun. Sensitive instruments show that this field is not constant and that it oscillates slightly in the course of each day. Occasionally, irregular fluctuations lasting for hours or even days become superposed on the normal oscillations. The intensity and the frequency of these disturbances are closely associated with sunspots. Figure 74 shows the striking agreement between the sunspot number and the so-called geomagnetic character figures recorded during the last hundred years. (The geomagnetic character figure is a quantitative measure of the fluctuations of the geomagnetic field in the course of one day.)

How can sunspots have so definite an effect on the earth's magnetic field? Though sunspots are gigantic magnets, it seems unlikely that their fields could reach the earth directly. Geomagnetic storms must therefore be caused by some intermediary between the sun and the earth. Today we know for certain that this intermediary is of a material nature—that it consists of highly rarefied currents and clouds of gas. These gases are expelled from the sun with velocities between 250 and 1000 miles a second and take between one and four days to reach the earth.

Magnetic storms

Large disturbances in the earth's magnetic field, called magnetic storms, usually take place one to two days after the appearance of large chromospheric flares of types 3 or 3 + (see page 108). This delay must be the result of the time it takes a cloud to travel from the sun. This is also borne out by the fact that the earth's external (measurable) magnetic field can only be changed by external electric currents (just as a compass needle changes its direction when an electric current is sent through a nearby wire). The mechanism of a magnetic storm must therefore be explained in roughly the fol-

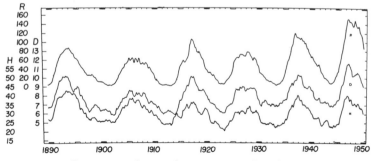

FIG. 74. Sunspot numbers and geomagnetic disturbances.

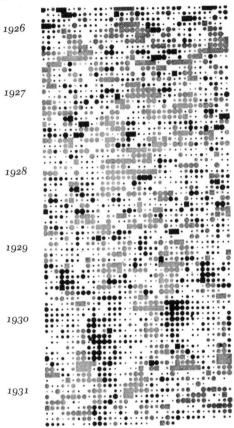

1926

1927

1928

1929

1930

1931

FIG. 75. Day by day record of geomagnetic activity (after Bartels).

lowing way: the sun expels a small cloud of gas with an explosive velocity of about 900 miles a second. As it travels through empty space this cloud keeps on expanding, until on approaching the earth it comes in contact with the earth's magnetic field. Now, since the gas in the cloud, like that in the solar corona, is completely ionized—since it consists of positive hydrogen nuclei (protons) and free electrons—its electric behavior can be likened to that of a large (compressible)

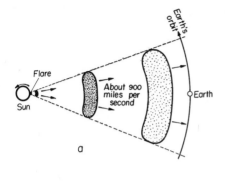

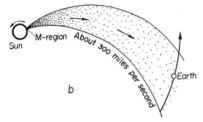

FIG. 76. Clouds of cor-
puscles and streams of
corpuscles from the sun.

block of metal. Just as a current is induced in a block
of metal or a coil of wire which is brought close to a
magnetic field, so the geomagnetic field now induces a
current in this gaseous conductor. The action of the
earth's magnetic field on this induced current causes
the cloud to hover some distance above the earth. The
induced current in the cloud then produces a magnetic
field of its own, which becomes superposed upon the
earth's field. The resulting increase in field intensity is
felt as a geomagnetic disturbance.

Corpuscular streams from the sun

Magnetic storms are relatively rare phenomena, small
fluctuations of the earth's magnetic field being far more
common. These fluctuations follow the strange pattern
shown in Figure 75. The darker and larger the mark
on the figure the greater the disturbance of the earth's

magnetic field. The diagram is so arranged that consecutive horizontal patterns represent differences of 27 days (that is, one solar rotation seen from the earth). In other words, the pattern makes it clear that geomagnetic disturbances and also their absence are often associated with the sun's rotation.

If our assumption about the nature of geomagnetic storms is correct, this would mean that the smaller fluctuations are not caused by individual clouds of gas but by a continuous stream of particles which brushes against the earth with every rotation of the sun (Fig. 76).

Although these streams of corpuscles cannot be observed directly—their density is extremely low—the theory seems to fit the facts. Probably these corpuscular streams are identical with the coronal rays shown in Figure 33. Thus, the earth's magnetic field enables us to deduce the presence in space of invisible coronal streams, just as the ionosphere enabled us to deduce the presence of invisible ultraviolet and X rays.

The auroras

Even the beautiful northern lights of our higher latitudes are due to corpuscles from the sun. Their appearance shows so remarkable a parallelism with geomagnetic disturbances that both must be attributed to the same cause. We cannot enter into a detailed discussion of the many beautiful forms the auroras take—beams of light or glowing arches, stable or changing patterns, long drapes or narrow strips of pulsating light colored flames or white sheets. In any case the details of the mechanism causing these phenomena at heights between 50 and 600 miles are not yet fully known. From spectra of the northern lights, which, because of their weak intensity, can only be photographed with very sensitive spectrographs, it appears that their light is largely concentrated in a few oxygen and nitrogen emission lines.

High-velocity hydrogen nuclei from the sun

The light from the aurora also emits hydrogen lines which could be due to our own upper atmosphere, were it not for the fact that the lines are displaced from their normal position in the spectrum toward the violet. This shift of the lines can only be the result of a Doppler effect, that is, of the great velocity with which these luminous hydrogen atoms are approaching the observer. Calculations show that their velocity is between 1250 and 2000 miles per hour, and perhaps even greater. This result is particularly important since it is our only direct proof of the existence of high-velocity solar corpuscles which are assumed to cause geomagnetic storms and the auroras. (It has now been shown that the characteristic features of the auroral spectrum can be reproduced by proton bombardment in the laboratory).

Unfortunately, our present understanding of the mechanism involved is still beset by a contradiction: the velocities of the solar protons deduced from the spectrum are considerably larger than those deduced from the duration of their journey. The solar corpuscles must therefore undergo further acceleration as they approach the earth, then penetrate the terrestrial atmosphere with an abnormally high velocity.

Though auroras usually occur in high latitudes, intense auroras can occasionally be seen as far south as the Mediterranean. Their frequency distribution can be represented by concentric rings about the magnetic poles of the earth. This must be considered another confirmation of our hypothesis that the corpuscles exciting these light phenomena are charged particles (protons and electrons) deflected by the earth's magnetic field and, in consequence, drawn toward the earth's magnetic poles. This conclusion, made almost a hundred years ago, has meanwhile been confirmed both by calculations and also by model experiments.

Conclusion

This discussion of the sun's effects on our nocturnal sky concludes our short excursion through the solar system. The smooth course of this journey, which led from the glowing interior of the sun to its coldest and outermost planets may have misled the reader into thinking that few problems remain to be solved. Fortunately, this is far from being the case. Simplified accounts like the present book must needs emphasize past achievements at the expense of a discussion of unsolved questions. For the astronomer, the inexhaustible store of problems in the world he has set out to conquer remains the real mainspring of all his arduous researches.

INDEX